INTRODUCTION TO THE METHODS OF REAL ANALYSIS

INTRODUCTION TO THE METHODS OF REAL ANALYSIS

MAURICE SION
University of British Columbia

Holt, Rinehart and Winston, Inc.
New York / Chicago / San Francisco / Atlanta / Dallas /
Montreal / Toronto / London

Library of Congress Catalog Card Number: 68-18380

2692408

Printed in the United States of America

1 2 3 4 5 6 7 8 9

TO
SARICA
Y
MAXICO

PREFACE

The material in this book is based on lectures given at the University of British Columbia as part of a year's course in analysis, normally taken by senior undergraduates and first-year graduate students.

The book is intended primarily for those students who are trying to pass from a sound but elementary and naïve view of limits, integration, and differentiation in Euclidean space to the more sophisticated points of view of modern point set topology and measure theory. It assumes only a fair understanding of the topology of the real line and facility with ϵ's and δ's. It is greatly concerned with training the student to become an active mathematician, and, hence, it aims to involve him as an active participant in the development of the field. For this reason, the emphasis is on the methods and ideas of real analysis, rather than on the collection of theorems, and many of the exercises are used as an integral part of the text. A conscious effort is made to use modern tools and sophisticated ideas in a context that is more or less elementary and still recognizable by the student, rather than older techniques in an abstract setting. The hope is that this will give the student a better appreciation of the power and beauty of current methods in the field. There is great stress on simplicity and economy of thought, especially in the definitions. Concepts are introduced from as intuitive a view as possible, and so as to stand on their own as much as possible. The paramount goal is to make the student appreciate the connection between concepts. Thus, the identification of different points of view is never carried out through definitions, only through theorems.

The book is divided into two parts along fairly natural lines. Part I concentrates on topological concepts, while Part II deals mainly with measure theory. In Part I, only that portion of elementary point set topology is developed which does not involve significant difficulties beyond those encountered in such classical spaces as $\mathscr{L}_p$, $\mathscr{L}_p$, $C[0;1]$ and the like. Similarly, in Part II, only that portion of measure theory is developed which does not involve significant difficulties beyond those encountered by Lebesgue-Stieltjes measures on the line and Lebesgue measure on $\mathscr{R}^n$.

In measure theory we use the Carathéodory process as the fundamental tool. Adoption of the Carathéodory approach enables us to bring quickly together the great many aspects of the theory that are responsible for its playing such a central role in analysis. Through this approach, its applicability to a wide variety of fields such as probability, functional analysis, real variables, and so on, is clearly spotlighted, and passage from one aspect to another is made both natural and simple. Of particular interest is the relation of measure theory to topology. From the Carathéodory point of view, the connection of a measure with the topology of the underlying space is direct rather than through the continuous functions. These and linear functionals may be studied for their own sake (as indeed they are in this text, and just as easily as from any point of view), but they need not clutter the picture in situations where they are irrelevant, for example, in establishing approximation properties of Lebesgue-Stieltjes measures, in discussing derivatives, length, area, probability, and the like. In fact, neither Borel sets nor continuous functions play any special roles in our treatment.

Vancouver, Canada
April 1968

M.S.

CONTENTS

Preface *vii*

PART I Topological Concepts

1 ■ ELEMENTS OF SET THEORY **3**

1. Introduction 3
2. Basic Notation 3
3. Relations and Functions 4
4. Set Operations 5
5. Countable Sets 6
6. Exercises 9

2 ■ SPACES OF FUNCTIONS **10**

1. Introduction 10
2. Some Classical Spaces 10
3. Vector Spaces 13
4. Metric Spaces 16
5. Exercises 18

3 ■ ELEMENTS OF POINT SET TOPOLOGY **20**

1. Introduction 20
2. Neighborhoods in Metric Spaces 20
3. Topologies 22
4. Hausdorff, Regular, Normal Topologies 25
5. Convergence 26
6. Countability Conditions 29
7. Completeness 31
8. Compactness 35
9. Baire Category 37
10. Connectedness 39
11. Miscellaneous Exercises 41

4 ■ CONTINUOUS FUNCTIONS **43**

1. Introduction 43
2. Continuity and Limits 43
3. Uniform Continuity 45
4. Homeomorphisms 46
5. Limits of Functions and Equicontinuity 47
6. Linear Functionals 51

PART II Measure Theory

5 ■ MEASURES ON ABSTRACT SPACES 57

1. Introduction 57
2. The Extended Real Line 57
3. Additive Functions and Families 58
4. Variation, Jordan Decomposition 63
5. Carathéodory Measures 65

6 ■ LEBESGUE-STIELTJES MEASURES 73

1. Introduction 73
2. Lebesgue-Stieltjes Measures on the Line 73
3. Lebesgue Measure on $\mathscr{R}^n$ 79

7 ■ INTEGRATION 84

1. Introduction 84
2. Concepts Involved in Lebesgue-Stieltjes Integration 84
3. Elementary Properties of the Integral 89
4. Limit Theorems 94
5. Fubini Theorem 96
6. Connections with Topology 100
7. Bird's Eye View of Various Approaches to Integration 103

8 ■ DIFFERENTIATION 106

1. Introduction 106
2. Radón-Nikodym Derivative 107
3. The Vitali Covering Theorem 112
4. Differentiation on the Line 114

9 ■ RIESZ REPRESENTATION 118

1. Introduction 118
2. Signed Measures 118
3. Functions of Bounded Variation 120
4. Linear Functionals on $\mathbf{C}_0$ 126

Symbols *129*

Index *132*

PART I.
TOPOLOGICAL CONCEPTS

1. ELEMENTS OF SET THEORY

1. INTRODUCTION

Nowadays the ideas of set theory permeate almost all branches of mathematics. This chapter introduces the basic set-theoretic notions, terminology, and notation used throughout the text and establishes a few elementary facts about countable sets which are needed later.

The notions of set and element of a set are taken as primitives. The terms set, collection, family, space are all taken to mean the same thing and will be used interchangeably. Typical examples: the set of all even numbers, the collection of all the books in some library, the family of all continuous real-valued functions on the unit interval, the space of all plane vectors having unit length. Also, to say that an object belongs to a set is equivalent to saying that it is an element of the set or that it is a point in the set.

2. BASIC NOTATION

The symbol "iff" stands for "if and only if."
The following are all definitions:

2.1. $x \in A$ iff x is an element of A.
2.2. $x \notin A$ iff x is not an element of A.
2.3. $A \subset B$ (read: A is contained in B or A is a subset of B) iff every element of A is also an element of B.
2.4. $A \supset B$ iff $B \subset A$.
2.5. $A = B$ iff $A \subset B$ and $B \subset A$.
2.6. $A \neq B$ iff it is not true that $A = B$.
2.7. ϕ denotes the empty set or set without any elements. It is characterized by the fact that, for every x, $x \notin \phi$.
2.8. $\{x, y, z, \cdots\}$ denotes the set whose only elements are those listed inside the brackets, that is, $x, y, z, \cdots$. Order and repetitions in listing the

elements are immaterial. Thus,

$$\{x, y\} = \{y, x\} = \{x, x, y\}.$$

Do not confuse $\{x\}$ with x (which may be a set itself).

2.9. $\{x: P(x)\}$ denotes the set of all x for which the proposition $P(x)$ is true. Example: $\{x: x < 0\}$ is the set of all negative numbers.

2.10. $\{x \in A: P(x)\}$ denotes the set of all x which belong to A and for which the proposition $P(x)$ is true.

2.11. For m, n integers,

$$\{m, \cdots, n\} = \{i: i \text{ is an integer and } m \leq i \leq n\}.$$

Note that if $n < m$, then $\{m, \cdots, n\} = \phi$.
We shall usually write $i = m, \cdots, n$ for $i \in \{m, \cdots, n\}$.

2.12. $\mathscr{R}$ denotes the set of all real numbers.
$\mathscr{R}_+$ denotes the set of all nonnegative numbers.

2.13. $[a; b] = \{x: a \leq x \leq b\}$.
$(a; b) = \{x: a < x < b\}$.
$[a; b) = \{x: a \leq x < b\}$.
$(a; b] = \{x: a < x \leq b\}$.

2.14. $\mathscr{R}a$ denotes the set of all rational numbers.
$\mathscr{R}a_+$ denotes the set of all nonnegative rational numbers.

2.15. ω denotes the set of all natural numbers $0, 1, 2, \cdots$.
ω_+ denotes the set of all positive natural numbers $1, 2, \cdots$.

3. RELATIONS AND FUNCTIONS

The formal mathematical method of associating y to x is to form the ordered pair (x, y). The notion of an ordered pair is taken here as a primitive. It is characterized by the property:

$$(x, y) = (x', y') \text{ iff } x = x' \quad \text{and} \quad y = y'.$$

The mathematical description of a rule which associates certain objects with others is the set of all ordered pairs (x, y) such that y is associated to x by the rule. For example, the rule which associates with each number its square is given by $\{(x, y): y = x^2\}$. This leads to the following definitions:

3.1. f is a relation iff f is a set of ordered pairs.

3.2. y is related to x by f or f makes y correspond to x iff $(x, y) \in f$.

3.3. domain $f = \{x: (x, y) \in f$ for some $y\}$.

3.4. range $f = \{y: (x, y) \in f$ for some $x\}$.

3.5. $f[A] = \{y: (x, y) \in f$ for some $x \in A\}$.

3.6. $f/A = \{(x, y): x \in A$ and $(x, y) \in f\}$.

3.7. $f^{-1} = \{(y, x): (x, y) \in f\}$.

3.8. $f \circ g = \{(x, z):$ for some y, $(x, y) \in g$ and $(y, z) \in f\}$.

3.9. f is a function iff f is a relation and for every $x \in$ domain f there is a unique y related to x by f, that is, for every x, y and y': $(x, y) \in f$ and $(x, y') \in f$ implies $y = y'$. This y is called the value of f at x and is denoted by $f(x)$ or f_x or f^x. If f and g are functions then $(f \circ g)(x) = f(g(x))$.

3.10. f is on A to B iff f is a function, domain $f = A$ and range $f \subset B$.

3.11. f is on A onto B iff f is a function, domain $f = A$ and range $f = B$.

3.12. f is one-to-one iff f is a function and f^{-1} is a function.

3.13. For m, n integers and f a function,

$$\{f(m), \cdots, f(n)\} = f[\{m, \cdots, n\}].$$

3.14. When it is well understood that we are working in some given nonempty space S, for any $a \in \mathscr{R}$ we shall denote by $\mathbf{a}$ the constant function on S to $\{a\}$, that is, $\mathbf{a}(x) = a$ for every $x \in S$.

4. SET OPERATIONS

The basic operations for constructing new sets from given ones are described in the following definitions.

4.1. Definition of union

(1) $A \cup B = \{x \colon x \in A \text{ or } x \in B\}$.

(2) $\bigcup_{i=m}^{n} A_i = \{x \colon x \in A_i \text{ for some } i = m, \cdots, n\}$

(3) $\bigcup_{i \in I} A_i = \{x \colon x \in A_i \text{ for some } i \in I\}$.

(4) $\bigcup F = \bigcup_{A \in F} A$.

(5) F covers A or F is a covering of A iff $A \subset \bigcup F$.

(6) F' is a subcovering of F iff $F' \subset F$ and $\bigcup F' = \bigcup F$.

(7) $\{A_i; i \in I\} = \{B \colon B = A_i \text{ for some } i \in I\}$.

(8) $\{A_i; i \in I \text{ and } P(i)\} = \{B \colon B = A_i$ for some $i \in I$ for which the proposition $P(i)$ is true$\}$.

Note that, for any index set I, if A_i is a set for every $i \in I$, that is, A is a set-valued function on I, then

$$\{A_i; i \in I\} = \bigcup_{i \in I} \{A_i\} = A[I].$$

Do not confuse $\bigcup_{i \in I} \{A_i\}$ with $\bigcup_{i \in I} A_i$ (see 2.8).

4.2. Definition of intersection

(1) $A \cap B = \{x \colon x \in A \text{ and } x \in B\}$.

(2) $\bigcap_{i=m}^{n} A_i = \{x \colon x \in A_i \text{ for } i = m, \cdots, n\}$.

(3) $\bigcap_{i \in I} A_i = \{x \colon x \in A_i \text{ for every } i \in I\}$.

(4) $\bigcap F = \bigcap_{A \in F} A$.

4.3. Definition of difference

$A \sim B = \{x \colon x \in A \text{ and } x \notin B\}$.

4.4. Definition of Cartesian product

$A \times B = \{(x, y)\colon\ x \in A \text{ and } y \in B\}.$

Some of the elementary properties of these set operations are listed in the theorems below. These theorems are used so frequently in mathematics that one seldom bothers to refer to them explicitly. They are straightforward consequences of the definitions, and their proofs are left as exercises for the reader (anyone having serious trouble checking these facts should study elementary logic).

4.5. Theorems

(1) $A \cap \bigcup_{i\in I} B_i = \bigcup_{i\in I} (A \cap B_i).$

(2) $A \cup \bigcap_{i\in I} B_i = \bigcap_{i\in I} (A \cup B_i).$

(3) $A \sim \bigcup_{i\in I} B_i = \bigcap_{i\in I} (A \sim B_i).$

(4) $A \sim \bigcap_{i\in I} B_i = \bigcup_{i\in I} (A \sim B_i).$

4.6. Theorems

For any relation f we have:

(1) $f[\bigcup_{i\in I} A_i] = \bigcup_{i\in I} f[A_i],$

(2) $f[\bigcap_{i\in I} A_i] \subset \bigcap_{i\in I} f[A_i],$

(3) $f[A \sim B] \supset f[A] \sim f[B].$

4.7. Theorems

For any function f we have:

(1) $f^{-1}[\bigcap_{i\in I} A_i] = \bigcap_{i\in I} f^{-1}[A_i],$

(2) $f^{-1}[A \sim B] = f^{-1}[A] \sim f^{-1}[B].$

4.8. Theorems

(1) $\bigcup_{i\in I} A_i \times B = \bigcup_{i\in I} (A_i \times B).$

$A \times \bigcup_{i\in I} B_i = \bigcup_{i\in I} (A \times B_i).$

(2) $\bigcap_{i\in I} (A_i \times B_i) = (\bigcap_{i\in I} A_i) \times (\bigcap_{i\in I} B_i).$

(3) $$(A \times B) \sim (A' \times B') = ((A \sim A') \times B) \cup ((A \cap A') \times (B \sim B'))$$
$$= (A \times (B \sim B')) \cup ((A \sim A') \times (B \cap B')).$$

5. COUNTABLE SETS

The idea of counting the elements of a set involves associating with each natural number an element of the set until the whole set has been exhausted. Allowing for poor counting due to repetitions and skipping of a few integers every now and then, but not missing any elements of the set, we see that what we have mathematically is a function whose domain is contained in the set of integers and whose range is the whole of the given set. A finite set is characterized by the fact that the counting eventually terminates. This leads us to the following definitions.

5.1. Definitions

Recall that ω denotes the set of all natural numbers.

(1) A is countable iff there exists a function f such that domain $f \subset \omega$ and range $f = A$. A is uncountable iff A is not countable.

(2) A is finite iff there exists a function f and $n \in \omega$ such that domain $f \subset \{0, \cdots, n\}$ and range $f = A$. A is infinite iff A is not finite.

(3) A has the same power as B iff there exists a one-to-one function on A onto B.

(4) A has n elements iff $n \in \omega$ and A has the same power as $\{1, \cdots, n\}$.

Note that if $f = \phi$, then f is one-to-one, domain $f = \phi$, and range $f = \phi$. Thus ϕ is finite and has 0 elements. We also have as an immediate consequence of the definitions that every finite set is countable. We list in the exercises some of the elementary properties of finite and countable sets. The properties of countable sets which concern us the most here are given in the following theorems.

5.2. Theorems. Let $A \subset B$ and f be a function on A.

(1) If B is countable, then $f[A]$ is countable.

(2) If B is finite, then $f[A]$ is finite.

■ **proof:** Suppose g is a function with domain $g \subset \omega$ and range $g = B$. Let $\alpha = g^{-1}[A]$ and, for $n \in \alpha$, $h(n) = f(g(n))$, that is, $h = f \circ (g/\alpha)$. Then domain $h \subset$ domain g and range $h = f[A]$. ■

5.3. Theorems. $\omega \times \omega$ is countable. Hence:

(1) if A and B are countable, then $A \times B$ is countable;

(2) if I is countable and, for every $i \in I$, A_i is countable, then $\bigcup_{i \in I} A_i$ is countable.

■ **proofs:** Let $f(m, n) = 2^m 3^n$. Then f is one-to-one on $\omega \times \omega$ to ω. Hence f^{-1} is a function, domain $f^{-1} \subset \omega$ and range $f^{-1} = \omega \times \omega$. Thus, $\omega \times \omega$ is countable.

(1) Suppose f and g are functions, $\alpha =$ domain $f \subset \omega$, $\beta =$ domain $g \subset \omega$, range $f = A$ and range $g = B$. For $m \in \alpha$ and $n \in \beta$, let $h(m, n) = (f(m), g(n))$. Then $\alpha \times \beta \subset \omega \times \omega$ and $h[\alpha \times \beta] = A \times B$. Since $\omega \times \omega$ is countable, by 5.2 it follows that $A \times B$ is countable.

(2) Let $\alpha \subset \omega$ and f be on α onto I. For each $i \in I$, let $\beta_i \subset \omega$ and x_i be on β_i onto A_i. Set

$$D = \{(m, n) \colon m \in \alpha \quad \text{and} \quad n \in \beta_{f(m)}\}$$

and for $(m, n) \in D$ let $g(m, n) = x_{f(m)}(n)$. Then $D \subset \omega \times \omega$ and $g[D] = \bigcup_{i \in I} A_i$. Hence by 5.2, $\bigcup_{i \in I} A_i$ is countable. ■

5.4. Theorem. A is countable iff A is finite or A has the same power as ω.

■ **proof:** If A is finite or has the same power as $\boldsymbol{\omega}$, then clearly A is countable. Suppose A is countable but not finite, and let $\alpha \subset \boldsymbol{\omega}$ and f be on α onto A. We shall construct by recursion a one-to-one function g on $\boldsymbol{\omega}$ onto A. Let k_0 be the smallest integer in α and set $g(0) = f(k_0)$. For any $n \in \boldsymbol{\omega}$, having defined $g(0), \cdots, g(n)$, we proceed to define $g(n+1)$ as follows. Since A is not finite, we have $A \sim \{g(0), \cdots, g(n)\} \neq \phi$. Let k_{n+1} be the smallest $i \in \alpha$ such that $f(i) \in A \sim \{g(0), \cdots, g(n)\}$ and set $g(n+1) = f(k_{n+1})$. Then $g(n+1) \neq g(m)$ for $m = 0, \cdots, n$. Thus, g is one-to-one, domain $g = \boldsymbol{\omega}$, and range $g \subset A$. We must actually have range $g = A$, for if $x \in A$ let i be the smallest integer in α with $f(i) = x$. Since $k_n < k_{n+1}$ for any $n \in \boldsymbol{\omega}$, we must have $i < k_n$ for some $n \in \boldsymbol{\omega}$ and hence $i = k_m$ for some $m < n$ so that $g(m) = f(k_m) = f(i) = x$ and $x \in$ range g. ■

The next theorems are two of the most commonly used tools for determining whether two sets have the same power. In particular, 5.5 can be used to show that the set of real numbers is not countable (exercise 6.12).

5.5. Theorems (Cantor). For any set S:

(1) $\{A : A \subset S\}$ has the same power as $\{f : f \text{ is on } S \text{ to } \{0, 1\}\}$.

(2) $\{A : A \subset S\}$ does not have the same power as S.

■ **proofs:**

(1) For each $A \subset S$, let $\mathbf{1}_A$ be the characteristic function of A, that is,

$$\mathbf{1}_A(x) = \begin{cases} 1 & \text{if} \quad x \in A \\ 0 & \text{if} \quad x \in S \sim A \end{cases}$$

Then $\mathbf{1}$ is one-to-one and, for any f on S to $\{0, 1\}$, if $A = f^{-1}[\{1\}]$ then $\mathbf{1}_A = f$.

(2) Suppose there exists a function f on S onto $\{A : A \subset S\}$. Let $A = \{x \in S : x \notin f(x)\}$. Then for some $a \in S$ we have $f(a) = A$ and therefore conclude that $a \in A$ iff $a \notin f(a) = A$, which is impossible. ■

5.6. Theorem (Cantor-Schröder-Bernstein). If A has the same power as a subset of B and B has the same power as a subset of A, then A has the same power as B.

■ **proof:** Let f be a one-to-one function on A to B and g be a one-to-one function on B to A. Define the sequences α and β by recursion as follows:

$$\alpha_o = A, \qquad \beta_o = B$$

$$\alpha_{n+1} = g[\beta_n], \qquad \beta_{n+1} = f[\alpha_n] \qquad \text{for } n \in \omega,$$

let:

$$A' = \bigcap_{n \in \omega} \alpha_n, \qquad B' = \bigcap_{n \in \omega} \beta_n,$$

and define the function h on A by

$$h(x) = \begin{cases} f(x) & \text{if } x \in (\alpha_{2n} \sim \alpha_{2n+1}) \quad \text{for some } n \in \omega \\ g^{-1}(x) & \text{if } x \in (\alpha_{2n+1} \sim \alpha_{2n+2}) \quad \text{for some } n \in \omega \\ f(x) & \text{if } x \in A'. \end{cases}$$

Then h is one-to-one and range $h = B$ since for every $n \in \omega$:

$$\alpha_{n+1} \subset \alpha_n,$$

$$f[\alpha_{2n} \sim \alpha_{2n+1}] = \beta_{2n+1} \sim \beta_{2n+2},$$

$$g^{-1}[\alpha_{2n+1} \sim \alpha_{2n+2}] = \beta_{2n} \sim \beta_{2n+1},$$

and

$$f[A'] = B'. \blacksquare$$

6. EXERCISES

1. Determine $\bigcup_{i \in \phi} A_i$ and $\bigcap_{i \in \phi} A_i$.
2. Prove theorems 4.5, 4.6, 4.7, 4.8.
3. A is finite iff, for some $n \in \boldsymbol{\omega}$, A has n elements. This n is unique.
4. If A and B are finite then $A \cup B$ and $A \times B$ are finite.
5. If I is finite and, for every $i \in I$, A_i is finite then $\bigcup_{i \in I} A_i$ is finite.
6. $\boldsymbol{\omega}$ is infinite.
7. A is infinite iff there exists $A' \subset A$ such that A' is countable and infinite.
8. A is infinite iff there exists $A' \subset A$, $A' \neq A$ such that A' has the same power as A.
9. The set of rational numbers is countable.
10. The set of algebraic numbers is countable.
11. If A is countable and $n \in \boldsymbol{\omega}$ then $\{x: x \text{ is on } \{0, \cdots, n\} \text{ to } A\}$ is countable.
12. The set of real numbers $\mathscr{R}$ is uncountable.
13. Let F be the family of open sets in $\mathscr{R}$, that is, sets A such that for every $x \in A$ there exists $r > 0$ with $(x - r; x + r) \subset A$. Then F has the same power as $\mathscr{R}$.

2. SPACES OF FUNCTIONS

1. INTRODUCTION

In analysis, one of the strongest motivations for considering spaces other than Euclidean space has been the study of limits of functions, especially in such fields as differential and integral equations. Some typical questions: Under what circumstances is the limit of continuous functions itself continuous? What properties do limits of continuous functions have? In trying to answer such questions, mathematicians have found it very convenient to consider various sets of functions or function spaces. Such spaces also arise very naturally when we use operational methods for solving linear differential equations. The differentiation operator D or some polynomial in D, involved in a differential equation, the Laplace transform are all functions whose domain and range are function spaces.

At first, function spaces were little more than a notational convenience. But soon people began to notice more and more striking resemblances between familiar concepts in Euclidean space and ideas they were using to get new results.

This led them to isolate and then systematically study some of the properties common to Euclidean space and to the function spaces they were considering. These abstractions have turned out to be extremely powerful tools and now form the basis for most work in analysis.

The purpose of this chapter is to introduce some of the well-known function spaces and isolate the notions of distance,vector, length of a vector, and inner product between vectors.

2. SOME CLASSICAL SPACES

Although hardly anyone visualizes Euclidean spaces of dimension greater than three, such spaces offer no conceptual difficulty to anyone who looks at a point in 3-space as a triple of real numbers. The passage from triple to

n-tuple is painless. The passage from finite- to infinite-dimensional vector spaces can also be made very simple and obvious if we look at an n-tuple in the proper way. The inductive definition of n-tuple as an ordered pair whose first element is an $(n-1)$-tuple is hard to extend. However, if we look at an n-tuple as a function x on $\{0, \cdots, n-1\}$, so that the ith coordinate of x, x_i, is simply the value of x at i, then the passage from finite- to infinite-dimensional vector is very simple. Replacing the domain $\{0, \cdots, n-1\}$ by any set A, we see that any function x on A can be considered as a vector with as many coordinates as there are points in A. For each $i \in A$, the ith coordinate of x is the functional value $x(i)$ or x_i. The dimension of the vector x is finite, countable or uncountable according to whether domain x is finite, countable, or uncountable. We also note that ordinary addition of real-valued functions and multiplication by constants coincide with coordinatewise addition of vectors and multiplication by scalars. Thus, spaces of real-valued functions on a set A may be considered as natural generalizations of Euclidean space. We now introduce some of these spaces.

2.1. Cartesian products

In the following definitions, we interpret a vector as a function and thereby introduce natural extensions of the notion of Cartesian product from the finite to the arbitrary case.

(1) x is an n-tuple in S iff $n \in \boldsymbol{\omega}$ and x is a function on $\{0, \cdots, n-1\}$ to S. x is a finite sequence in S iff, for some $n \in \boldsymbol{\omega}$, x is an n-tuple in S. For any function x and $n \in \boldsymbol{\omega}$, we write $(x_0, \cdots, x_n)$ for $x/\{0, \cdots, n\}$.

(2) For $n \in \boldsymbol{\omega}$:

$$S^n = \{x\colon x \text{ is an } n\text{-tuple in } S\}.$$

Thus, $\mathscr{R}^n$ is n-dimensional Euclidean space.

(3) For m, n integers:

$$\prod_{i=m}^{n} S_i = \{x\colon x \text{ is a function on } \{m, \cdots, n\} \text{ and } x_i \in S_i \text{ for } i = m, \cdots, n\}.$$

More generally, for any set I:

(4) $$S^I = \{x\colon x \text{ is a function on } I \text{ to } S\}.$$

(5) $$\prod_{i \in I} S_i = \{x\colon x \text{ is a function on } I \text{ and } x_i \in S_i \text{ for } i \in S\}.$$

2.2. Spaces of sequences

We might be tempted to consider the space of all sequences in $\mathscr{R}$ as the most immediate generalization of Euclidean space. However, if we try to extend the definitions of inner product and length to sequences by using formulas similar to those used in $\mathscr{R}^n$, we find ourselves concerned about the convergence of such expressions as $\Sigma_i x_i y_i$ and $\Sigma_i x_i^2$. Such concern leads us to consider spaces of sequences satisfying certain convergence conditions, the so-called ℓ_p spaces. In the following definitions, we introduce these spaces along with subspaces which can be naturally identified with Euclidean spaces.

(1) x is a sequence in S iff x is a function on $\boldsymbol{\omega}$ to S, that is, $x \in S^{\omega}$. y is a subsequence of x iff x and y are sequences and, for every $n \in \boldsymbol{\omega}$, there exists $k_n \in \boldsymbol{\omega}$ with $k_n < k_{n+1}$ and $y_n = x_{k_n}$.

(2) For $n \in \boldsymbol{\omega}$:

$$\mathscr{R}_n = \{x \in \mathscr{R}^{\omega} : x_i = 0 \quad \text{for} \quad i \geq n, \, i \in \boldsymbol{\omega}\}.$$

Thus, $\mathscr{R}_n$ can be identified in an obvious way with $\mathscr{R}^n$.

(3) $\ell_0 = \bigcup_{n \in \omega} \mathscr{R}_n$.
For $0 < p < \infty$:
$\ell_p = \{x \in \mathscr{R}^{\omega} : \Sigma_{i \in \omega} |x_i|^p < \infty\}$.
$\ell_\infty = \{x \in \mathscr{R}^{\omega} : \sup_{i \in \omega} |x_i| < \infty\}$.
Thus, for $n \in \boldsymbol{\omega}$ and $0 \leq p \leq q \leq \infty$ we have

$$\mathscr{R}_n \subset \mathscr{R}_{n+1} \subset \ell_p \subset \ell_q.$$

Of the ℓ_p spaces, ℓ_1, ℓ_2, and ℓ_∞ are by far the most widely used ones.

(4) The ℓ_p-norm, $\|x\|_p$, for $x \in \ell_p$ is given by:

$$\|x\|_p = \left(\sum_{i \in \omega} |x_i|^p\right)^{1/p} \qquad \text{for } 1 \leq p < \infty,$$

$$\|x\|_\infty = \sup_{i \in \omega} |x_i|.$$

We do not define it for $0 < p < 1$ by the above formula because in this case it does not satisfy the triangle inequality:

$$\|x + y\|_p \leq \|x\|_p + \|y\|_p.$$

[Try $p = \frac{1}{2}$, $x = (0, 1)$, $y = (1, 0)$].
The ℓ_∞-norm is also called the sup norm (see 2.3.1).

(5) For $x, y \in \mathscr{R}^{\omega}$, the standard inner product $\langle x, y \rangle$ is defined by

$$\langle x, y \rangle = \sum_{i \in \omega} x_i y_i$$

whenever the sum on the right exists.

2.3. Spaces of continuous functions

The set of all continuous functions on [0, 1] is one of the most widely investigated spaces in analysis. It has spawned several major fields of study; in fact most of what is known as functional analysis has its roots in this space. In the following definitions we introduce generalizations of this space and some important subspaces.

(1) $\mathbf{B}(S) = \{x\colon x \text{ is on } S \text{ to } \mathscr{R} \text{ and } \sup_{s\in S} |x(s)| < \infty\}$.

The sup norm $\|x\|_\infty$ for $x \in \mathbf{B}(S)$ is defined by

$$\|x\|_\infty = \sup_{s\in S} |x(s)|.$$

(2) $\mathbf{C}(S) = \{x\colon x \text{ is a continuous function on } S \text{ to } \mathscr{R}\}$.

This space is defined for any S for which there is a notion of a continuous function on S to $\mathscr{R}$. As we shall see in Chapter 4, this is defined for any topological space. Until then the reader may restrict S to a subset of Euclidean space.

(3) For $n \in \boldsymbol{\omega}_+$ and S an open rectangle in Euclidean space:

$$\mathbf{C}^n(S) = \{x\colon x \text{ is on } S \text{ to } \mathscr{R} \text{ and } x \text{ has continuous derivatives up to order } n\}.$$

(4) For S an open rectangle in Euclidean space:

$$\mathbf{C}^\infty(S) = \{x\colon x \text{ is on } S \text{ to } \mathscr{R} \text{ and } x \text{ has continuous derivatives of all orders}\}.$$

3. VECTOR SPACES

Each function space introduced in Sections 2.2 and 2.3 has the property that the sum of any two of its elements and the product of one of its elements by a real number are all still elements of the space. This and some of the properties of addition and multiplication are abstracted into the following definition.

3.1. Definition

V is a vector space under $(+, \cdot, \ominus)$ iff $\ominus \in V$ and for every $x, y, z \in V$ and $a, b \in \mathscr{R}$ we have:

(i) $x + y = y + x \in V$,
(ii) $x + (y + z) = (x + y) + z$,
(iii) $x + \ominus = x$,
(iv) there exists $(-x) \in V$ such that $x + (-x) = \ominus$,
(v) $a \cdot x \in V$,
(vi) $a \cdot (b \cdot x) = (a \cdot b) \cdot x$,
(vii) $(a + b) \cdot x = (a \cdot x) + (b \cdot x)$,
(viii) $a \cdot (x + y) = (a \cdot x) + (a \cdot y)$,
(ix) $1 \cdot x = x$.

Next, the essential properties of length or norm of a vector and of inner product of two vectors for the development of a theory similar to that in Euclidean space are incorporated in the following definitions.

3.2. Definitions

For V a vector space under $(+, \cdot, \ominus)$:

(1) P is a pseudonorm on V iff P is a function on V such that for every $x, y \in V$ and $a \in \mathscr{R}$:

(a) $0 \leq P(x) < \infty$,
(b) $P(a \cdot x) = |a| \cdot P(x)$,
(c) $P(x + y) \leq P(x) + P(y)$.

P is a norm on V or V is a normed space under P iff P is a pseudonorm on V and, for every $x \in V$,

(d) $P(x) = 0$ implies $x = \ominus$.

(2) B is a bilinear form on V iff B is on $V \times V$ to $\mathscr{R}$ such that, for $x, y, z \in V$ and $a, b \in \mathscr{R}$:

(a) $B(a \cdot x + b \cdot y, z) = a \cdot B(x, z) + b \cdot B(y, z)$,
(b) $B(x, a \cdot y + b \cdot z) = a \cdot B(x, y) + b \cdot B(x, z)$.

B is a symmetric bilinear form on V iff B is a bilinear form on V and, for every $x, y \in V$:

(c) $B(x, y) = B(y, x)$.

(3) B is a pseudo-inner product on V iff B is a symmetric bilinear form on V such that, for every $x \in V$,

(a) $B(x, x) \geq 0$.

B is an inner product on V iff B is a pseudo-inner product on V and, for every $x \in V$,

(b) $B(x, x) = 0$ implies $x = \ominus$.

(4) P is the pseudonorm on V induced by B iff B is a pseudo-inner product on V and, for every $x \in V$,

$$P(x) = \sqrt{B(x, x)}.$$

The fundamental relation between inner product and norm is given in theorem 3.3.

3.3. Theorems. Let V be a vector space under $(+, \cdot, \ominus)$, B be a pseudo-inner product on V and $P(x) = \sqrt{B(x, x)}$ for every $x \in V$. Then:

(1) (Cauchy-Schwarz inequality). For every $x, y \in V$,

$$|B(x, y)| \leq P(x) \cdot P(y).$$

(2) P is a pseudonorm on V. It is actually a norm on V iff B is an inner product on V.

■ **proofs**

(1) For any $x, y \in V$,

$$0 \leq P^2(x \pm y) = B(x \pm y, x \pm y) = P^2(x) \pm 2B(x, y) + P^2(y).$$

Hence

$$|B(x, y)| \leq \tfrac{1}{2}(P^2(x) + P^2(y)).$$

If $P(x) = 0$ then, for every $a > 0$, $P(a \cdot x) = 0$, and hence $|B(a \cdot x, y)| \leq \frac{1}{2}P^2(y)$ so that $|B(x, y)| \leq (1/2a)P^2(y)$ and therefore $B(x, y) = 0$. If $P(x) \neq 0$ and $P(y) \neq 0$, let

$$x' = \frac{1}{P(x)} \cdot x \quad \text{and} \quad y' = \frac{1}{P(y)} \cdot y.$$

Then $P(x') = P(y') = 1$ and

$$\frac{1}{P(x) \cdot P(y)} |B(x, y)| = |B(x', y')| \leq \tfrac{1}{2}(P^2(x') + P^2(y')) = 1.$$

Thus

$$|B(x, y)| \leq P(x) \cdot P(y).$$

(2) For any $x, y \in V$ and $a \in \mathscr{R}$ we have

$$P(a \cdot x) = \sqrt{B(a \cdot x, a \cdot x)} = |a| \cdot \sqrt{B(x, x)} = |a| \cdot P(x),$$

$$P^2(x + y) = B(x + y, x + y) = P^2(x) + 2B(x, y) + P^2(y)$$
$$\leq P^2(x) + 2P(x) \cdot P(y) + P^2(y) = (P(x) + P(y))^2. \blacksquare$$

In case x and y are nonzero vectors in the plane and θ is the angle between them, we know from the law of cosines that θ is related to the standard inner product by the formula

$$\cos \theta = \frac{\langle x, y \rangle}{|x| \cdot |y|}.$$

This suggests defining the angle θ between any two nonzero elements x, y in a vector space having an inner product B and norm P generated by B by

$$\cos \theta = \frac{B(x, y)}{P(x)P(y)}$$

The Cauchy-Schwarz inequality guarantees that the number on the right is between -1 and 1, and hence the definition is possible.

One of the first applications of the Cauchy-Schwarz inequality was to show that the ℓ_2-norm is indeed a norm on ℓ_2 (exercise 5.3). One can check directly that the ℓ_1 and ℓ_∞-norms are also norms (exercises 5.1, 5.2). However, to check that the ℓ_p-norm is a norm for $1 < p < \infty$ (exercise 5.4) one needs the following theorem.

3.4. Theorem. Let $n \in \boldsymbol{\omega}_+$, $p > 1$, $q > 1$, $1/p + 1/q = 1$, and $x, y \in \mathscr{R}_n$. Then (referring to 2.2 for definitions of standard inner product and ℓ_p-norm) we have:

(1) (Hölder's inequality) $|\langle x, y \rangle| \leq \|x\|_p \, \|y\|_q$.

(2) (Minkowski's inequality) $\|x + y\|_p \leq \|x\|_p + \|y\|_p$.

■ **proofs:** We first show that for $a, b \in \mathscr{R}_+$ we have

$$ab \leq \frac{a^p}{p} + \frac{b^q}{q}.$$

To this end, let $f(x) = x^{p-1}$ and note that f is monotone increasing and that $f^{-1}(y) = y^{q-1}$. Suppose $f(a) \leq b$. Then $a \leq f^{-1}(b) = b^{q-1}$ and for $a \leq x \leq b^{q-1}$ we have $f(x) \leq b$, hence

$$\int_a^{b^{q-1}} x^{p-1}\,dx \leq b(b^{q-1} - a),$$

$$\frac{b^{(q-1)p}}{p} - \frac{a^p}{p} \leq b^q - ab,$$

and since $pq = p + q$,

$$ab \leq \frac{a^p}{p} + b^q - \frac{b^q}{p} = \frac{a^p}{p} + \frac{b^q}{q}.$$

If $b \leq f(a)$, apply the same argument to f^{-1}, for then $f^{-1}(b) \leq a$.

(1) To check Hölder's inequality, suppose $\|x\|_p \neq 0$, $\|y\|_q \neq 0$ and let $x' = \dfrac{x}{\|x\|_p}$, $y' = \dfrac{y}{\|y\|_q}$. Then $\|x'\|_p = 1$ and $\|y'\|_q = 1$ and:

$$\frac{1}{\|x\|_p} \cdot \frac{1}{\|y\|_q} |\langle x, y\rangle| = |\langle x', y'\rangle| = \sum_{i=0}^{n-1} |x_i' y_i'|$$

$$\leq \sum_{i=0}^{n-1} \left(\frac{|x_i'|^p}{p} + \frac{|y_i'|^q}{q}\right) = \frac{1}{p} + \frac{1}{q} = 1.$$

(2) We get Minkowski's inequality by applying Hölder's inequality in the second step below:

$$\sum_{i=0}^{n-1} |x_i + y_i|^p \leq \sum_{i=0}^{n-1} (|x_i| \cdot |x_i + y_i|^{p-1} + |y_i| \cdot |x_i + y_i|^{p-1})$$

$$\leq (\|x\|_p + \|y\|_p)\left(\sum_{i=0}^{n-1} |x_i + y_i|^{(p-1)q}\right)^{1/q}$$

$$= (\|x\|_p + \|y\|_p)\left(\sum_{i=0}^{n-1} |x_i + y_i|^p\right)^{1/q}.$$

Hence

$$\|x + y\|_p = \left(\sum_{i=0}^{n-1} |x_i + y_i|^p\right)^{1-1/q} \leq \|x\|_p + \|y\|_p. \ \blacksquare$$

4. METRIC SPACES

We indicated earlier that one of the main reasons for considering generalizations of Euclidean space is the study of limits of functions. Now, even a superficial examination shows that the definition of limit in Euclidean space is based entirely on the notion of distance between points. A more careful analysis reveals that in fact a great deal of the theory of convergence makes use of only a few properties of Euclidean distance. These are isolated in the definition of metric given below.

4.1. Definition

ρ is a pseudometric on S or S is a pseudometric space under ρ iff ρ is a function on $S \times S$ such that for every $x, y, z \in S$:

(i) $0 \leq \rho(x, y) = \rho(y, x) < \infty$,
(ii) $\rho(x, z) \leq \rho(x, y) + \rho(y, z)$,
(iii) $\rho(x, x) = 0$.

ρ is a metric on S or S is a metric space under ρ iff ρ is a pseudometric on S and, for $x, y \in S$,
(iv) $\rho(x, y) = 0$ implies that $x = y$.

Now, once the notion of distance has been abstracted into a metric, all concepts defined solely in terms of distance automatically extend to the more general situation. In the next definitions we list a few of the more obvious ones.

4.2. Definitions

For any pseudometric ρ on S:

(1) The open sphere of radius r about x is

$$\mathbf{S}_\rho(r, x) = \{y: \rho(x, y) < r\}.$$

(2) The diameter of a set $A \subset S$ is

$$\operatorname{diam}_\rho A = \begin{cases} \sup \{\rho(x, y); x \in A \text{ and } y \in A\} & \text{if } A \neq \phi \\ 0 \quad \text{if } A = \phi. \end{cases}$$

(3) A is bounded in ρ iff $\operatorname{diam}_\rho A < \infty$.

(4) A is totally bounded in ρ iff, for every $r > 0$, there exists a finite $B \subset S$ such that $A \subset \bigcup_{x \in B} \mathbf{S}_\rho(r, x)$.

(5) For $\phi \neq A \subset S$ and $\phi \neq B \subset S$, the distance between A and B is

$$\operatorname{dist}_\rho (A, B) = \inf \{\rho(x, y); x \in A \text{ and } y \in B\}.$$

We shall frequently drop explicit reference to ρ in the above notation when there is no danger of confusion.

In Euclidean space, the notion of distance can be derived from that of length. We use the same method in the next definition to introduce a translation-invariant metric in any normed space.

4.3. Definition

For any pseudonorm P on a vector space V, the pseudometric ρ induced by P is the function on $V \times V$ such that for $x, y \in V$

$$\rho(x, y) = P(x - y).$$

The reader should check readily that ρ is indeed a pseudometric and that it is a metric if and only if P is a norm.

Thus, we can introduce a metric in each of the function spaces defined in Section 2 of this chapter. By applying the theory which we develop in Chapter 3 to various function spaces, we obtain results about limits of functions. The type of limit involved depends on the metric used. For example, in $\mathbf{C}([0; 1])$ and ℓ_∞, by using the metric induced by the sup norm we discuss uniform convergence. Since $\ell_1 \subset \ell_2 \subset \ell_\infty$, we may use in ℓ_1 the metric induced by the ℓ_1 or ℓ_2 or ℓ_∞-norm and thereby get results involving mean convergence or square mean convergence or uniform convergence. A statement such as, "A is dense in B," says that any function in B can be approximated, in the sense determined by the metric, by some function in A. Thus, the theory of metric spaces not only generalizes results about Euclidean space, but brings under one discipline many seemingly unrelated fields.

5. EXERCISES

1. The sup norm is a norm on $\mathbf{B}(S)$ and hence on any subspace of $\mathbf{B}(S)$, for instance, ℓ_∞ and $\mathbf{C}([0; 1])$. Note that the sup norm of a function is small if and only if the function is uniformly small in absolute value.
2. The ℓ_1-norm is a norm on ℓ_1.
3. Use the Cauchy-Schwarz inequality to check that
   (i) ℓ_2 is a vector space,
   (ii) if $B(x, y) = \langle x, y\rangle$, then B is an inner product on ℓ_2,
   (iii) the ℓ_2-norm is a norm on ℓ_2.
4. Use the Minkowski inequality to check that, for $1 < p < \infty$, ℓ_p is a vector space and the ℓ_p-norm is a norm on ℓ_p.
5. In $\mathscr{R}_3$, describe the unit sphere $\mathbf{S}(1, \mathbf{0})$ for each of the metrics induced by the ℓ_1, ℓ_2, and ℓ_∞-norms.
6. Let $n \in \boldsymbol{\omega}_+$ and V be the restriction to $[0; 1]$ of all functions in $\mathbf{C}^n(\mathscr{R})$. For $x \in V$, let $x^{(i)}$ be the ith derivative of x and

$$P(x) = \sum_{i=0}^{n} \sup \{|x^{(i)}(t)|; t \in [0; 1]\}.$$

   Show that P is a norm on V.
7. Let $1 \leq p \leq q < \infty$ and $x \in \ell_p$. Show that
   (i) $\|x\|_\infty \leq \|x\|_q \leq \|x\|_p$,
   (ii) $\|x\|_\infty = \lim_q \|x\|_q$.

8. Referring to the ordinary Riemann integral for bounded functions, let

$$S_1 = \left\{x \in \mathbf{B}([0;1]) : \int_0^1 x(t)\,dt \text{ exists}\right\},$$

$$S_2 = \left\{x \in \mathbf{B}([0;1]) : \int_0^1 |x(t)|^2\,dt \text{ exists}\right\},$$

$$P_1(x) = \int_0^1 |x(t)|\,dt, \qquad P_2(x) = \left(\int_0^1 |x(t)|^2\,dt\right)^{1/2}.$$

Using the ordinary addition of functions for "+" and multiplication by a constant for "·" check that:

(a) S_1 is a vector space under $(+, \cdot, \mathbf{0})$ and P_1 is a pseudonorm, but not a norm, on S_1.

(b) $\mathbf{C}([0;1])$ is a vector subspace of S_1 and the restriction of P_1 to this space is actually a norm.

(c) S_2 is not a vector space under $(+, \cdot, \mathbf{0})$.

(d) If $B(x, y) = \int_0^1 x(t)y(t)\,dt$ then B is a pseudo-inner product on S_1 and is an inner product on $\mathbf{C}([0;1])$.

(e) P_2 is a norm on $\mathbf{C}([0;1])$.

3. ELEMENTS OF POINT SET TOPOLOGY

1. INTRODUCTION

In this chapter we develop some of the fundamental tools for discussing convergence. We do this within a set theoretic framework which borrows heavily from our geometric intuition of Euclidean space. Much of the terminology in fact is suggested by geometric pictures. Although our primary interest is in metric spaces, we develop a fair amount of the theory in more general topological spaces. However, in the nonmetric situation, we confine ourselves to results whose extension from the metric case is effortless. The greater generality not only gives us better perspective, but quite often leads to simpler proofs.

An example of a situation which leads us to consider nonmetric spaces is a space of bounded real-valued functions: whereas the metric induced by the sup norm allows us to study uniform convergence, in general, no metric will help us study ordinary pointwise convergence. This example is taken up in several exercises. Note also that if the functions are not bounded, then even the sup norm will not lead to a metric space.

2. NEIGHBORHOODS IN METRIC SPACES

The starting point for defining limits in Euclidean space, say the plane, is the notion of "y is near x." A set theoretic translation of this idea is that y belongs to a circle about x. Equally reasonable translations are obtained if we replace circle by square or rectangle or triangle or ellipse. In fact, many developments of calculus in the plane use squares or rectangles. It is not hard to check directly that the definition of limit is the same no matter which of these types of region is used for a neighborhood of x. We feel intuitively that the shape of the region *per se* is not significant in the notion of neighborhood.

What is important is that x be "strictly inside" or an "interior point" of the region so that there be room inside to put a circle about x (and hence also a rectangle, triangle, ellipse, or other type of region). This leads us to the following definitions.

2.1. Definitions

For any pseudometric ρ on S, $x \in S$ and $A \subset S$:

(1) x is an interior point of A or A is a neighborhood of x in ρ iff, for some $r > 0$, $\mathbf{S}_\rho(r, x) \subset A$.

interior$_\rho$ $A = \{x: x$ is an interior point of A in $\rho\}$.

nbhd$_\rho$ $x = \{A: A$ is a neighborhood of x in $\rho\}$.

Having settled on a notion of neighborhood, we now introduce a few related concepts:

(2) x is a boundary point of A in ρ iff every neighborhood of x in ρ contains points in A and points outside A, that is, for every $B \in \text{nbhd}_\rho x$, $B \cap A \neq \phi$ and $B \sim A \neq \phi$.

boundary$_\rho A = \{x: x$ is a boundary point of A in $\rho\}$.

Note that a boundary point of A is automatically also a boundary point of $(S \sim A)$ and need not belong to A. In general, a set may contain only a portion of its boundary. The extreme cases where a set contains none or all of its boundary turn out to be the most interesting and are isolated in the following definitions.

(3) A is open in ρ iff $A \cap \text{boundary}_\rho A = \phi$.
(4) A is closed in ρ iff $\text{boundary}_\rho A \subset A$.
(5) $\text{closure}_\rho A = A \cup \text{boundary}_\rho A$.

Again we may drop all explicit reference to ρ in the above notations when there is no danger of confusion.

The essential properties of open and of closed sets are given in the next theorems. These follow immediately from the definitions and the proofs are left as exercises.

2.2. Theorems. Let ρ be a pseudometric on S, $\mathcal{G}$ be the family of open sets in ρ and $\mathcal{F}$ the family of closed sets in ρ. Then:

(1) $A \in \mathcal{G}$ iff $S \sim A \in \mathcal{F}$.
(2) $\phi \in \mathcal{G} \cap \mathcal{F}$ and $S \in \mathcal{G} \cap \mathcal{F}$.
(3) If $G \subset \mathcal{G}$, then $\bigcup G \in \mathcal{G}$.
(4) If $\phi \neq F \subset \mathcal{F}$, then $\bigcap F \in \mathcal{F}$.
(5) If $\phi \neq G \subset \mathcal{G}$ and G is finite, then $\bigcap G \in \mathcal{G}$.
(6) If $F \subset \mathcal{F}$ and F is finite, then $\bigcup F \in \mathcal{F}$.

2.3. Exercises

1. Let $A = \{(1/m, 1/n); m \in \omega_+ \text{ and } n \in \omega_+\}$. Using the standard metric for the plane, find: interior A, boundary A, closure A.
2. Let $A = \{(x, y): x + y > 1\}$. Using the standard metric for the plane, check that A is open and find closure A.

In the following exercises, suppose S is a pseudometric space under ρ and $A \subset S$:

3. A is open iff $A =$ interior A.
4. A is closed iff $A =$ closure A.
5. boundary $A =$ closure $A \sim$ interior A.
6. closure $A = \bigcap\{B: B \text{ is closed and } A \subset B\}$.
7. $\mathbf{S}(r, x)$ is open for any $x \in S$ and $r \in \mathscr{R}$.
8. $A \in$ nbhd x iff, for some open B, $x \in B \subset A$.
9. interior $A = \bigcup\{B: B \text{ is open and } B \subset A\}$.
10. Let $x \in S$, $r \geq 0$, and $A = \{y: \rho(x, y) \leq r\}$. Then A is closed, but we need not have $A =$ closure $\mathbf{S}(r, x)$ for any $r \geq 0$.
11. closure $A = \{x: \text{dist}(\{x\}, A) = 0\}$.
12. For any $r \geq 0$, $\{x: \text{dist}(\{x\}, A) < r\}$ is open and $\{x: \text{dist}(\{x\}, A) \leq r\}$ is closed.
13. diam $A =$ diam closure A.
14. For any $x, y \in S$:
    (a) $\rho(x, y) = 0$ iff nbhd $x =$ nbhd y
    (b) $\rho(x, y) \neq 0$ iff there exist $A \in$ nbhd x and $B \in$ nbhd y with $A \cap B = \phi$.

3. TOPOLOGIES

It should be clear from theorems 2.2 and the exercises in 2.3 that the notions of neighborhood, boundary, closure, open set, and closed set are so interrelated that any one of them could be derived from any of the others. After decades of trying all sorts of possibilities, it seems simplest to base the development of the theory of convergence on open sets. One reason for this is that it is possible to go very far using only the properties of open sets listed in theorems 2.2. Thus, we can start with any space S and family $\mathscr{G}$ having these properties and develop a good portion of the theory without any reference to how the family $\mathscr{G}$ came about. Such a family is called a topology and a topological space then is a generalization of a metric space.

3.1. Definitions

(1) $\mathscr{G}$ is a topology on S or S is a topological space under $\mathscr{G}$ iff $\mathscr{G}$ is a family of subsets of S such that:
   (i) $\phi, S \in \mathscr{G}$;
   (ii) if $G \subset \mathscr{G}$, then $\bigcup G \in \mathscr{G}$;
   (iii) if $\phi \neq G \subset \mathscr{G}$ and G is finite, then $\bigcap G \in \mathscr{G}$.

(2) For any topology $\mathscr{G}$ on S and $A \subset S$, the restriction of $\mathscr{G}$ to A or the relative topology of $\mathscr{G}$ to A is $\{A \cap U; U \in \mathscr{G}\}$.

(3) For any pseudometric ρ on S:
$\mathscr{G}$ is the topology induced by ρ iff $\mathscr{G} = \{A: A \text{ is open in } \rho\}$.

(4) The pseudometrics ρ and ρ' on S are equivalent iff they induce the same topology, that is,

$$\{A: A \text{ is open in } \rho\} = \{A: A \text{ is open in } \rho'\}.$$

(5) $\mathscr{G}$ is a pseudometric topology iff, for some pseudometric ρ, $\mathscr{G}$ is the topology induced by ρ. $\mathscr{G}$ is a metric topology iff, for some metric ρ, $\mathscr{G}$ is the topology induced by ρ.

(6) For any pseudonorm P on a vector space S:
$\mathscr{G}$ is the topology induced by P iff $\mathscr{G}$ is the topology induced by the pseudometric induced by P.

(7) Two pseudonorms are equivalent iff they induce the same topology.

(8) $\mathscr{G}$ is a pseudonorm topology iff, for some pseudonorm P, $\mathscr{G}$ is the topology induced by P. $\mathscr{G}$ is a norm topology iff, for some norm P, $\mathscr{G}$ is the topology induced by P.

Notational Convention: In all subsequent concepts involving a topology $\mathscr{G}$, we may replace $\mathscr{G}$ by a pseudometric ρ or a pseudonorm P whenever $\mathscr{G}$ is induced by ρ or by P. Also, we may drop explicit reference to $\mathscr{G}$ or ρ or P when there is no danger of confusion.

We now make use of the results in 2.2 and 2.3 to introduce in a topological space the notions discussed in the previous section for a metric space.

3.2. Definitions

For any topology $\mathscr{G}$ on S:

(1) A is open in $\mathscr{G}$ iff $A \in \mathscr{G}$.
(2) A is closed in $\mathscr{G}$ iff $S \sim A \in \mathscr{G}$.
(3) closure A in $\mathscr{G} = \bigcap\{B: B \text{ is closed in } \mathscr{G} \text{ and } A \subset B\}$.
(4) interior A in $\mathscr{G} = \{\bigcup B: B \text{ is open in } \mathscr{G} \text{ and } B \subset A\}$.
(5) boundary A in $\mathscr{G}$ = closure A in $\mathscr{G} \sim$ interior A in $\mathscr{G}$.
(6) A is a neighborhood of x in $\mathscr{G}$ iff $x \in$ interior A in $\mathscr{G}$.
(7) nbhd x in $\mathscr{G} = \{A: A \text{ is a neighborhood of } x \text{ in } \mathscr{G}\}$.

In the following theorems we list the main elementary properties of the sets defined above.

3.3. Theorems. For any topology on S and $A \subset S$:

(1) A is open iff A = interior A iff $A \cap$ boundary $A = \phi$.
(2) If F is a nonempty family of closed sets, then $\bigcap F$ is closed.
(3) If F is a finite family of closed sets then $\bigcup F$ is closed.

(4) A is closed iff $A =$ closure A iff boundary $A \subset A$.
(5) $x \in$ closure A iff, for every $B \in$ nbhd x, $B \cap A \neq \phi$.
(6) $x \in$ boundary A iff, for every $B \in$ nbhd x, $B \cap A \neq \phi$ and $B \sim A \neq \phi$.
(7) interior $(S \sim A) = S \sim$ closure A.
(8) closure closure $A =$ closure A.
(9) If F is a finite family of subsets of S, then

$$\text{closure} \bigcup_{A \in F} A = \bigcup_{A \in F} \text{closure } A.$$

■ **proof:** Parts (1) through (8) are direct consequences of the definitions and previous results and are left as exercises. To check (9), let $C = \bigcup_{A \in F}$ closure A. From the definition and (2), closure A is closed for each $A \in F$ and hence, by (3), C is closed. Since, $A \subset$ closure A, we have $\bigcup F \subset C$ and hence closure $\bigcup F \subset C$. On the other hand, for each $A \in F$, $A \subset \bigcup F$, and hence closure $A \subset$ closure $\bigcup F$ and therefore

$$\bigcup_{A \in F} \text{closure } A \subset \text{closure} \bigcup F.$$

Thus, $C =$ closure $\bigcup F$. ■

3.4. Exercises

1. For any space S, let $\mathscr{G}_1 = \{\phi, S\}$ and $\mathscr{G}_2 = \{A : A \subset S\}$. Check that $\mathscr{G}_1$ and $\mathscr{G}_2$ are topologies induced by pseudometrics. $\mathscr{G}_1$ and $\mathscr{G}_2$ are known respectively as the trivial and discrete topologies.
2. In $\mathscr{R}_3$, the metrics induced by the ℓ_1, ℓ_2 and ℓ_∞-norms are equivalent.
3. In ℓ_1, the metrics induced by the ℓ_1, ℓ_2, ℓ_∞-norms are not equivalent.
4. Let $S = \mathbf{B}([0; 1])$. For $T \subset [0; 1]$, $r > 0$, $x \in S$, let

$$V(T, r, x) = \{y \in S : |x(t) - y(t)| < r \text{ for every } t \in T\}.$$

Interpreting $V(T, r, x)$ as a "(T, r)-sphere about x," let $\mathscr{G}_1$, $\mathscr{G}_2$, $\mathscr{G}_3$ be the families of subsets A of S satisfying, for every $x \in A$, respectively conditions (1), (2), (3) below:
(1) there exist finite $T \subset [0; 1]$ and $r > 0$ with $V(T, r, x) \subset A$.
(2) there exist $T \subset [0; 1]$ and $r > 0$ with $V(T, r, x) \subset A$.
(3) there exists $r > 0$ with $V([0; 1], r, x) \subset A$.
Show that $\mathscr{G}_1$, $\mathscr{G}_2$, $\mathscr{G}_3$ are topologies and
(a) $\mathscr{G}_1 \subset \mathscr{G}_2 = \mathscr{G}_3$
(b) $\mathscr{G}_3$ is induced by the sup norm on S.
(c) $y \in$ closure A in $\mathscr{G}_3$ iff y can be approximated uniformly by some function in A.
(d) $y \in$ closure A in $\mathscr{G}_1$ iff y can be approximated pointwise (at any finite number of points) by some function in A.
$\mathscr{G}_1$ and $\mathscr{G}_3$ are referred to respectively as the topologies of pointwise and of uniform convergence on S.
(e) $\mathscr{G}_1 \neq \mathscr{G}_3$, in fact, find $A \subset \mathbf{C}([0; 1])$ so that closure A in $\mathscr{G}_1 \neq$ closure A in $\mathscr{G}_3$.

4. HAUSDORFF, REGULAR, AND NORMAL TOPOLOGIES

In the following definitions we isolate three fundamental properties possessed by metric and pseudometric topologies.

4.1. Definitions. For any topology $\mathscr{G}$ on S and $S' \subset S$:

(1) $\mathscr{G}$ is Hausdorff iff, for every $x, y \in S$ with $x \neq y$, there exist $U \in \text{nbhd } x$ in $\mathscr{G}$ and $V \in \text{nbhd } y$ in $\mathscr{G}$ with $U \cap V = \phi$.
S' is Hausdorff in $\mathscr{G}$ iff the restriction of $\mathscr{G}$ to S' is Hausdorff.

(2) $\mathscr{G}$ is regular iff, for every A closed in $\mathscr{G}$ and $x \in S \sim A$, there exist U, V open in $\mathscr{G}$ with $A \subset U$, $x \in V$, and $U \cap V = \phi$.
S' is regular in $\mathscr{G}$ iff the restriction of $\mathscr{G}$ to S' is regular.

(3) $\mathscr{G}$ is normal iff, for every A, B closed in $\mathscr{G}$ with $A \cap B = \phi$, there exist U, V open in $\mathscr{G}$ with $A \subset U$, $B \subset V$, and $U \cap V = \phi$.
S' is normal in $\mathscr{G}$ iff the restriction of $\mathscr{G}$ to S' is normal.

Note that in general the three conditions are not related, but if sets consisting of single points are closed, then the conditions are progressively stronger. Our interest in them is motivated by the following theorems.

4.2. Theorems. Let ρ be a pseudometric on S and $\mathscr{G}$ be the topology induced by ρ. Then

(1) $\mathscr{G}$ is normal,
(2) $\mathscr{G}$ is regular,
(3) $\mathscr{G}$ is Hausdorff iff ρ is a metric.

■ **proof**

(1) If A and B are closed and $A \cap B = \phi$, let

$$U = \{x\colon \text{dist}(\{x\}, A) < \text{dist}(\{x\}, B)\}$$

$$V = \{x\colon \text{dist}(\{x\}, B) < \text{dist}(\{x\}, A)\}.$$

In view of exercise 2.3.11 we have $A \subset U$, $B \subset V$, and clearly $U \cap V = \phi$. To see that U is open, let $x \in U$ and $r = \frac{1}{3}(\text{dist}(\{x\}, B) - \text{dist}(\{x\}, A))$. If $\rho(x, y) < r$, then for any $a \in A$ and $b \in B$ we have $\rho(a, y) < \rho(a, x) + r$ and $\rho(b, y) > \rho(b, x) - r$. Hence

$$\text{dist}(\{y\}, A) \leq \text{dist}(\{x\}, A) + r < \text{dist}(\{x\}, B) - r \leq \text{dist}(\{y\}, B).$$

Thus $S(x, r) \subset U$. Similarly, we see that V is open. Theorems (2) and (3) are immediate consequences of exercises 2.3.11 and 2.3.14. ■

By taking complements of closed sets, one checks immediately the following reformulations of regularity and normality.

4.3. Theorems. For any topology $\mathscr{G}$:

(1) $\mathscr{G}$ is regular iff, for every open A and $x \in A$, there exists open U with $x \in U \subset \text{closure } U \subset A$.

(2) $\mathscr{G}$ is normal iff, for every closed A and open B with $A \subset B$, there exists open U with $A \subset U \subset \text{closure } U \subset B$.

The three conditions discussed in this section are part of a series of separation axioms that can be imposed on a topology. The most important of these turns out to be regularity. It seems to be needed in almost any significant situation, whereas normality is a rather strong condition easily lost when Cartesian products are formed. Hausdorff topologies, on the other hand, have been grossly overrated, mainly for historical reasons. They are seldom essential, except possibly for uniqueness of limits (see the next section). As we shall see, for most of the theory the condition that a topology be Hausdorff is totally irrelevant, and assuming it when it is not needed never simplifies a proof. When confronted with a pseudometric space, such as an $\mathscr{L}_p$ space (discussed in the measure theory part, see also exercise 5.8 of Chapter 2), many people will apply exercise 4.4.1 below and construct an associated metric space made up of equivalence classes. We find it a lot easier to visualize two points zero distance apart than to integrate an equivalence class. The construction of such an artificial space is all the more undesirable when it is unnecessary.

4.4. Exercises

1. Let ρ be a pseudometric on S. For each $x \in S$, let $x^* = \{y: \rho(x, y) = 0\}$ and $S' = \{x^*; x \in S\}$. For $x, y \in S$ let $\rho'(x^*, y^*) = \rho(x, y)$. Show that ρ' is well defined on $S' \times S'$ and that it is a metric on S'.
2. The topology of pointwise convergence on $\mathbf{B}([0; 1])$ (see exercise 3.4.4) is Hausdorff and regular.
3. In the Euclidean plane, let
$$A = \{(x, y): y = 0\} \quad \text{and} \quad B = \{(x, y): x \cdot y = 1\}.$$
Find a continuous function f on the plane such that $f(x, y) = 0$ for $(x, y) \in A$ and $f(x, y) = 1$ for $(x, y) \in B$.
4. Let ρ be a pseudometric on S such that, for every $x \in S$, $\{x\}$ is closed in ρ. Then ρ is a metric on S.
5. If $\mathscr{G}$ is a Hausdorff topology on S then, for every $x \in S$, $\{x\}$ is closed in $\mathscr{G}$. However, the converse need not hold.

5. CONVERGENCE

In this section we consider two ways of approaching a point in a topological space. One is a direct, unordered way through a set and gives rise to the notion of accumulation point of a set. The other is a more restricted way through a sequence and gives rise to the notion of limit of a sequence.

5.1. Definitions

For any topology $\mathscr{G}$ on a space S, $A \subset S$ and $x \in S$:

(1) x is an isolated point of A in $\mathscr{G}$ iff $x \in A$ and there exists $U \in$ nbhd x in $\mathscr{G}$ with $A \cap U = \{x\}$.
(2) A is perfect in $\mathscr{G}$ iff A is closed and has no isolated points in $\mathscr{G}$.
(3) x is an accumulation point of A in $\mathscr{G}$ iff, for every $U \in$ nbhd x in $\mathscr{G}$, there exists $y \in A \cap U$ with $x \neq y$.

Note that adding to or removing a given point from a set does not affect its status as an accumulation point of the set. As immediate consequences of the definitions, we have the following theorems, which are left as exercises.

5.2. Theorems. Let $\mathscr{G}$ be any topology on S and $A \subset S$. Then

(1) For every $x \in S \sim A$, x is an accumulation point of A iff x is a boundary point of A.
(2) A is closed iff A contains all its accumulation points.
(3) closure $A = A \cup \{x\colon x$ is an accumulation point of $A\}$.
(4) If x is an accumulation point of A and the topology $\mathscr{G}$ is Hausdorff then, for every $U \in$ nbhd x, $A \cap U$ is infinite.
(5) If A is perfect, $A \neq \phi$ and $\mathscr{G}$ is Hausdorff, then A is infinite.

(Note that in (4) and (5) instead of "$\mathscr{G}$ is Hausdorff," all we need is that, for every $x, y \in S$ with $x \neq y$, there exists $U \in$ nbhd x with $y \notin U$.)

We consider next limits of sequences.

5.3. Definitions

For any topology $\mathscr{G}$ on a space S and sequence x in S:

(1) l is a limit point of x in $\mathscr{G}$ iff, for every $U \in$ nbhd l in $\mathscr{G}$ and $k \in \boldsymbol{\omega}$, there exists $n \in \boldsymbol{\omega}$ with $n \geq k$ and $x_n \in U$.
(2) x converges to l or $x_n \xrightarrow{n} l$ in $\mathscr{G}$ iff, for every $U \in$ nbhd l in $\mathscr{G}$, there exists $k \in \boldsymbol{\omega}$ such that, for every $n \in \boldsymbol{\omega}$, if $n \geq k$ then $x_n \in U$. In case x converges to a unique l we shall denote l by $\lim_n x_n$.
(3) x converges in $\mathscr{G}$ iff, for some $l \in S$, $x_n \xrightarrow{n} l$ in $\mathscr{G}$.

Note that a sequence may have more than one limit point (for example, $x_n = (-1)^n$ for $n \in \boldsymbol{\omega}$). Even if it has only one, it may not converge (for instance, $x_{2n} = n$ and $x_{2n+1} = 1$ for $n \in \boldsymbol{\omega}$). On the other hand, it may converge to more than one point (for example, in case of a pseudometric which is not a metric). However, if the topology is Hausdorff, then convergent sequences have unique limits.

We see from theorem 5.2.2 above that any topology is characterized by the notion of accumulation point of a set. Unfortunately, nonmetric topologies cannot always be characterized in terms of limits of sequences (see exercise 5.5.1). The restrictions of countability and strong sense of order among integers prove too much of a handicap in the general situation. To overcome such a handicap, generalizations of the notion of a sequence (for example, nets, filters, runs) have been introduced, but these are beyond the scope of this text.

5.4. Theorems. Let ρ be a pseudometric on S and $A \subset S$. With respect to the topology induced by ρ we have:

(1) For any sequence x in S, $x_n \xrightarrow{n} l$ iff $\lim_n \rho(l, x_n) = 0$.

(2) For any sequence x in S, l is a limit point of x iff there exists a subsequence y of x with $y_n \xrightarrow{n} l$.

(3) For any sequence x in S, $x_n \xrightarrow{n} l$ iff, for every subsequence y of x, $y_n \xrightarrow{n} l$.

(4) l is an accumulation point of A iff there exists a sequence x in $A \sim \{l\}$ with $x_n \xrightarrow{n} l$. (Note that a limit point of a sequence need not be an accumulation point of the range of the sequence).

(5) A is closed iff, for every sequence x in A and $l \in S$, if $x_n \xrightarrow{n} l$, then $l \in A$.

(6) closure $A = A \cup \{l\colon$ for some sequence x in A, $x_n \xrightarrow{n} l\}$.

(7) A is open iff, for every sequence x converging to some point in A, there exists $k \in \boldsymbol{\omega}$ such that, for every $n \in \boldsymbol{\omega}$, if $n \geq k$ then $x_n \in A$.

■ **proofs**

(1) Immediate from the definitions.

(2) Suppose l is a limit point of the sequence x. Let $k_0 = 0$ and for every $n \in \boldsymbol{\omega}$ let k_{n+1} be the smallest $j \in \boldsymbol{\omega}$ such that $j > k_n$ and $\rho(l, x_j) < 1/(n + 1)$. Such integers exist from the definition of limit point. Let $y_n = x_{k_n}$ for $n \in \boldsymbol{\omega}$. Then y is a subsequence of x and for any $n \in \boldsymbol{\omega}_+$, $\rho(l, y_n) < 1/n$ so that $y_n \xrightarrow{n} l$. The converse is immediate.

(3) Follows directly from the definitions.

(4) Let l be an accumulation point of A. For each $n \in \boldsymbol{\omega}$, choose $x_n \in A$ so that $x_n \neq l$ and $\rho(l, x_n) < 1/(n + 1)$. Then $x_n \xrightarrow{n} l$.

(5), (6), (7) Follow from the above and previous theorems. ■

We should point out that the results in 5.4 above not only enable us to discuss a pseudometric topology in terms of limits of sequences, but conversely they give us a method for deciding in some cases that a topology cannot be induced by any pseudometric (see exercise 5.5.1 below).

5.5. Exercises

1. Let $S = \mathbf{B}([0; 1])$ and $\mathscr{G}$ be the topology of pointwise convergence on S (see exercise 3.4.4). Let A be the family of all functions $x \in S$ such that,

for some finite $T \subset [0; 1]$,

$$x(t) = \begin{cases} 0 & \text{if} \quad t \in T \\ 1 & \text{if} \quad t \in [0; 1] \sim T. \end{cases}$$

Then $\mathbf{0}$ is an accumulation point of A, but no sequence in A converges to $\mathbf{0}$ in $\mathscr{G}$. Thus, $\mathscr{G}$ cannot be induced by any pseudometric on S.

2. The topology of pointwise convergence on $\mathbf{C}([0; 1])$ cannot be induced by any metric on $\mathbf{C}([0; 1])$. (See exercise 1).
3. If $\mathscr{G}$ is a Hausdorff topology on S and $A \subset S$, then $\{x \in S: x$ is an accumulation point of $A\}$ is closed.

6. COUNTABILITY CONDITIONS

In analysis on the real line, the rationals and intervals with rational end points play major roles. In this section we isolate some of the properties which make these sets so useful.

6.1. Definitions

For any topology $\mathscr{G}$ on a space S:

(1) A is dense in $\mathscr{G}$ iff $A \subset S$ and $S =$ closure A in $\mathscr{G}$.
(2) F is an open covering in $\mathscr{G}$ iff $F \subset \mathscr{G}$ and $S = \bigcup F$.
(3) $\mathscr{B}$ is a base for $\mathscr{G}$ iff $\mathscr{B} \subset \mathscr{G}$ and, for every $U \in \mathscr{G}$ and $x \in U$, there exists $V \in \mathscr{B}$ with $x \in V \subset U$.

6.2. Definitions

For any topology $\mathscr{G}$ on a space S and $A \subset S$:

(1) $\mathscr{G}$ is separable iff there exists a countable D such that D is dense in $\mathscr{G}$.
A is separable in $\mathscr{G}$ iff the restriction of $\mathscr{G}$ to A is separable.
(2) $\mathscr{G}$ is Lindelöf iff every open covering in $\mathscr{G}$ has a countable subcovering.
A is Lindelöf in $\mathscr{G}$ iff the restriction of $\mathscr{G}$ to A is Lindelöf.
(3) $\mathscr{G}$ has a countable base or satisfies the second axiom of countability iff there exists a countable $\mathscr{B}$ such that $\mathscr{B}$ is a base for $\mathscr{G}$.
A satisfies the second axiom of countability in $\mathscr{G}$ or $\mathscr{G}$ has a countable base on A iff the restriction of $\mathscr{G}$ to A has a countable base.

The fundamental relations among the three countability conditions are given in the following theorems.

6.3. Theorems. Let $\mathscr{G}$ be any topology on a space S.

(1) If $\mathscr{G}$ has a countable base, then $\mathscr{G}$ is separable and Lindelöf.
(2) If $\mathscr{G}$ is a pseudometric topology then:
$\mathscr{G}$ has a countable base iff $\mathscr{G}$ is separable iff $\mathscr{G}$ is Lindelöf.

■ **proofs**

(1) Let $\mathscr{B}$ be a countable base for $\mathscr{G}$. For each nonempty $V \in \mathscr{B}$, let $x_V \in V$ and $D = \{x_V;\ V \in \mathscr{B} \sim \{\phi\}\}$. Then D is countable and dense in $\mathscr{G}$. To check that $\mathscr{G}$ is Lindelöf, let F be any open covering and set $\mathscr{B}' = \{V \in \mathscr{B}\colon$ for some $A \in F,\ V \subset A\}$. Then, for each $x \in S$, there exists $A \in F$ with $x \in A$ and hence, since $\mathscr{B}$ is a base for $\mathscr{G}$, there exists $V \in \mathscr{B}$ with $x \in V \subset A$. Thus, $\mathscr{B}'$ covers S. For each $V \in \mathscr{B}'$, choose $A_V \in F$ so that $V \subset A_V$ and let $F' = \{A_V;\ V \in \mathscr{B}'\}$. Since $\mathscr{B}'$ is countable and covers S, the same is true of F'. Thus, F has a countable subcovering.

(2) Suppose $\mathscr{G}$ is induced by a pseudometric ρ so that, for each $x \in S$ and $r > 0$, the sphere $\mathbf{S}(r, x)$ is well defined. If $\mathscr{G}$ is separable, let D be countable and dense in $\mathscr{G}$ and $\mathscr{B} = \{\mathbf{S}(1/n, d);\ n \in \boldsymbol{\omega}_+$ and $d \in D\}$. Then $\mathscr{B}$ is countable and is a base for $\mathscr{G}$ since, for any $x \in S$ and $U \in \text{nbhd}\ x$, there exists $n \in \boldsymbol{\omega}_+$ with $\mathbf{S}(1/n, x) \subset U$ and $d \in D$ with $\rho(x, d) < 1/2n$ so that $x \in \mathbf{S}(1/2n, d) \subset \mathbf{S}(1/n, x) \subset U$ and $\mathbf{S}(1/2n, d) \in \mathscr{B}$. If $\mathscr{G}$ is Lindelöf, for each $n \in \boldsymbol{\omega}_+$, let $F_n = \{\mathbf{S}(1/n, x);\ x \in S\}$. Since F_n is an open covering, let F'_n be a countable subcovering and $\mathscr{B} = \bigcup_{n \in \omega} F'_n$. Then $\mathscr{B}$ is countable and is a base for $\mathscr{G}$ since, for any $x \in S$ and $U \in \text{nbhd}\ x$, there exists $n \in \boldsymbol{\omega}_+$ with $\mathbf{S}(1/n, x) \subset U$ and $A \in F'_{2n}$ with $x \in A$, that is, for some $y \in S$, $A = \mathbf{S}(1/2n, y)$ and $\rho(x, y) < 1/2n$ and hence $x \in \mathbf{S}(1/2n, y) \subset \mathbf{S}(1/n, x) \subset U$. ■

Hereditary properties of the countability conditions are given in the next theorems.

6.4. Theorems. Let $\mathscr{G}$ be any topology on S.

(1) If $\mathscr{G}$ has a countable base and $A \subset S$, then $\mathscr{G}$ has a countable base on A (thus, in view of 6.3, any subspace of a separable pseudometric space is separable).

(2) If $\mathscr{G}$ is Lindelöf and A is closed in $\mathscr{G}$, then A is Lindelöf in $\mathscr{G}$.

■ **proofs**

(1) If $\mathscr{B}$ is a countable base for $\mathscr{G}$ then $\{A \cap U;\ U \in \mathscr{B}\}$ is a countable base for $\mathscr{G}$ restricted to A.

(2) If F is a family of open sets covering A and A is closed, let $F' = F \cup \{S \sim A\}$. Then F' is an open covering. If $\mathscr{G}$ is Lindelöf, then F' has a countable subcovering and, since $S \sim A$ does not help cover A, a countable subfamily of F covers A. ■

We conclude with two important consequences of countability conditions.

6.5. Theorem (Weierstrass). For any topology on S, if $A \subset S$ is uncountable and Lindelöf (in particular, if A is an uncountable subset of a separable pseudometric space), then there exists $x \in A$ such that, for every $U \in \text{nbhd } x$,

$$A \cap U \text{ is uncountable.}$$

■ **proof:** If, for every $x \in A$, there exists $U_x \in \text{nbhd } x$ such that $A \cap U_x$ is countable then, since A is Lindelöf, a countable number of the U_x cover A and A is therefore countable, contradicting the hypothesis. ■

6.6. Theorem (Cantor-Bendixon). Let S be a separable pseudometric space and $A \subset S$. If A is closed, then there exists $A' \subset A$ such that A' is perfect and $A \sim A'$ is countable.

■ **proof:** Let $A' = \{x\colon \text{for every } U \in \text{nbhd } x, A \cap U \text{ is uncountable}\}$. If A is closed, then $A' \subset A$. Also, if x is an accumulation point of A', then clearly $x \in A'$ so that A' is closed. We see that A' has no isolated points, for if $x \in A'$ and $U \in \text{nbhd } x$ then, since $A \cap U \sim \{x\}$ is uncountable, by 6.5 there exists $y \in A' \cap U \sim \{x\}$. Thus A' is perfect. Finally $A \sim A'$ is countable, for otherwise by 6.5 again there would be $x \in A \sim A'$ such that $x \in A'$ which is impossible. ■

6.7. Exercises

1. Check directly, without using 6.4, that the set of irrationals on the line is separable in the standard metric.
2. Let $1 \leq p < \infty$, $S = \ell_p$ and $\mathscr{G}$ be the topology induced by the ℓ_p-norm. Check that ℓ_0 is dense in $\mathscr{G}$ and that S is separable in $\mathscr{G}$.
3. ℓ_∞ is not separable in the topology induced by the ℓ_∞-norm.
4. Let $S = \mathbf{C}([0; 1])$ and $\mathscr{G}$ be the topology on S induced by the sup norm. Then S is separable in $\mathscr{G}$.
5. For any pseudometric ρ on S, if A is totally bounded in ρ, then A is separable in ρ.
6. Let $\mathscr{G}$ be the standard topology in the plane. The families of open circles or ellipses or rectangles or squares are all bases for $\mathscr{G}$.
7. Let $S = [0; 1)$ and $\mathscr{G}$ be the family of all $A \subset S$ such that, for every $x \in A$ there exists $y > x$ with $[x; y) \subset A$. Then $\mathscr{G}$ is a topology on S and $\{[x; y);\ x \in S, y \in S \text{ and } x < y\}$ is a base for $\mathscr{G}$. Check that $\mathscr{G}$ is Hausdorff and separable, but does not have a countable base. Thus, $\mathscr{G}$ is not a metric topology.
8. Let $S = [0; 1]$ and $\mathscr{G} = \{A\colon A \subset S \text{ and either } 0 \notin A \text{ or } S \sim A \text{ is finite}\}$. Check that $\mathscr{G}$ is a topology on S, $\mathscr{G}$ is Hausdorff and Lindelöf (in fact any open covering has a finite subcovering), but $\mathscr{G}$ is not separable.

7. COMPLETENESS

A fundamental property of the real line is that it has no holes. This guarantees the convergence of many important sequences (for example, bounded monotone) and hence the solution of a great many equations. This property, based on the notion of Cauchy sequence and known as completeness, is hard to formulate in general topological spaces. In pseudometric spaces, however, its definition is an immediate extension of that on the real line.

7.1. Definitions

For any pseudometric ρ on a space S and $A \subset S$:

(1) x is a Cauchy sequence in ρ iff x is a sequence in S and for every $r > 0$, there exists $N \in \boldsymbol{\omega}$ such that, for every $m, n \in \boldsymbol{\omega}$, if $m > N$ and $n > N$, then $\rho(x_m, x_n) < r$.

(2) ρ is complete iff every Cauchy sequence in ρ converges in ρ. A is complete in ρ iff $\rho/(A \times A)$ is complete, that is, every Cauchy sequence in A converges to a point in A.

We now list some of the main properties of completeness.

7.2. Theorem. For any pseudometric ρ on S:

S is complete iff, for every sequence F of closed sets, if $\phi \neq F_{n+1} \subset F_n$ for $n \in \boldsymbol{\omega}$ and $\lim_n \operatorname{diam} F_n = 0$, then $\bigcap_{n\in\omega} F_n \neq \phi$.

■ **proof:** Let S be complete and F be a descending sequence of nonempty closed sets with $\lim_n \operatorname{diam} F_n = 0$. For each $n \in \boldsymbol{\omega}$ let, $x_n \in F_n$. Since for $m < n$ we have $x_n \in F_m$ and $\rho(x_m, x_n) \leq \operatorname{diam} F_m$, we see that x is a Cauchy sequence and hence x converges to some $l \in S$. For every $U \in \text{nbhd } l$ and $N \in \boldsymbol{\omega}$, there exists $n > N$ with $x_n \in U$ and, since $x_n \in F_n \subset F_N$, we have $U \cap F_N \neq \phi$ and therefore $l \in$ closure $F_N = F_N$. Thus, $l \in \bigcap_{N\in\omega} F_N$.

Conversely, if x is a Cauchy sequence, for each $n \in \boldsymbol{\omega}$ let $F_n =$ closure $\{x_i; i \in \omega, i \geq n\}$. Then F_n is closed, $\phi \neq F_{n+1} \subset F_n$ and (by exercise 2.3.13) $\lim_n \operatorname{diam} F_n = 0$. If $l \in \bigcap_{n\in\omega} F_n$, then, for every $n \in \boldsymbol{\omega}$, $\rho(l, x_n) \leq \operatorname{diam} F_n$ so that $x_n \xrightarrow{n} l$. ■

7.3. Theorems. Let ρ be a pseudometric and A be complete in ρ.

(1) If B is closed, then $A \cap B$ is complete.

(2) $l \in$ closure A iff, for some $l' \in A$, $\rho(l, l') = 0$.

(3) closure A is complete.

■ **proofs**

(1) Let x be a Cauchy sequence in $A \cap B$. Since A is complete, x converges to some $l \in A$ and, since B is closed, $l \in B$.

(2) By 5.4.6, $l \in$ closure A iff some sequence x in A converges to l. Since every convergent sequence is a Cauchy sequence and A is complete, there exists $l' \in A$ such that x converges to l'. Hence $\rho(l, l') = 0$.

(3) Let x be a Cauchy sequence in closure A. Using (2), for each $n \in \boldsymbol{\omega}$, let $x'_n \in A$ and $\rho(x_n, x'_n) = 0$. Then x' is a Cauchy sequence in A and

hence, for some $l \in A$, x' converges to l, that is, $\lim_n \rho(x'_n, l) = 0$. Since $\rho(x'_n, l) = \rho(x_n, l)$ we must have x converging to l. ∎

7.4. Theorems. Let ρ be a metric and A be complete in ρ. Then:

(1) A is closed.

(2) If A is perfect and $A \neq \phi$, then A is uncountable.

∎ **proofs:** Note that, since ρ is a metric, the topology induced by ρ is Hausdorff and regular.

(1) By 7.3.2, closure $A = A$.

(2) Let A be perfect and $A \neq \phi$. Then, there exist $x_0, x_1 \in A$ with $x_0 \neq x_1$. Choose disjoint closed neighborhoods $U(0)$, $U(1)$ of x_0 and x_1 respectively with diam $U(i) < 1$ for $i = 0, 1$. Since x_0 is an accumulation point of A, there exist $x_{00}, x_{01} \in A \cap U(0)$ with $x_{00} \neq x_{01}$. Choose disjoint closed neighborhoods $U(0, 0)$ and $U(0, 1)$ of x_{00} and x_{01}, respectively, so that $U(0, i) \subset U(0)$ and diam $U(0, i) < \frac{1}{2}$ for $i = 0, 1$. Similarly choose disjoint closed neighborhoods $U(1, 0)$ and $U(1, 1)$ so that $U(1, i) \subset U(1)$ and diam $U(1, i) < \frac{1}{2}$ for $i = 0, 1$. Proceeding by recursion, for each $n \in \boldsymbol{\omega}$ and finite sequence $(k_0, \cdots, k_n)$ with $k_i \in \{0, 1\}$ for $i = 0, \cdots, n$, choose a closed neighborhood $U(k_0, \cdots, k_n)$ so that: $U(k_0, \cdots, k_n) \cap A \neq \phi$, $U(k_0, \cdots, k_n, 0) \cap U(k_0, \cdots, k_n, 1) = \phi$, $U(k_0, \cdots, k_n, k_{n+1}) \subset U(k_0, \cdots, k_n)$ and diam $U(k_0, \cdots, k_n) < 1/(n + 1)$. Since A is complete, for each sequence $k \in \{0, 1\}^\omega$, by 7.2, there exists $x_k \in A \cap \bigcap_{n\in\omega} U(k_0, \cdots, k_n)$. If $l \in \{0, 1\}^\omega$ and $k \neq l$ then, for some $n \in \boldsymbol{\omega}$, $k_n \neq l_n$ and $U(k_0, \cdots, k_n) \cap U(l_0, \cdots, l_n) = \phi$ and hence $x_k \neq x_l$. Since $\{0, 1\}^\omega$ is uncountable, A must be uncountable. ∎

7.5. Theorem. For any pseudometric ρ on a space S there exists a pseudometric ρ' on a space S' such that: $S \subset S'$, $\rho'/(S \times S) = \rho$, S is dense in ρ' and S' is complete in ρ'. If ρ is a metric on S, then ρ' and S' can be chosen so that ρ' is a metric on S' (S' is called the completion of S).

∎ **proof:** Let T be the set of all Cauchy sequences in ρ and for $x, y \in T$ let $d(x, y) = \lim_n \rho(x_n, y_n)$. We first check that $d(x, y) < \infty$ by showing that the $\rho(x_n, y_n)$ form a Cauchy sequence of real numbers. Indeed, for any $r > 0$, there exists $N \in \boldsymbol{\omega}$ such that, for every $m, n \in \boldsymbol{\omega}$, if $m > N$ and $n > N$, then $\rho(x_m, x_n) < r$ and $\rho(y_m, y_n) < r$, hence

$$\rho(x_n, y_n) \leq \rho(x_n, x_m) + \rho(x_m, y_m) + \rho(y_m, y_n) < \rho(x_m, y_m) + 2r$$

and therefore $|\rho(x_n, y_n) - \rho(x_m, y_m)| < 2r$. Next, we check that d is a pseudometric, since clearly $0 \leq d(x, y) = d(y, x)$ and for $z \in T$:

$$\begin{aligned} d(x, z) &= \lim_n \rho(x_n, z_n) \leq \lim_n (\rho(x_n, y_n) + \rho(y_n, z_n)) \\ &= \lim \rho(x_n, y_n) + \lim \rho(y_n, z_n) = d(x, y) + d(y, z). \end{aligned}$$

Finally, to check that T is complete, let u be a Cauchy sequence in T. For each $k \in \boldsymbol{\omega}$, since u_k is a Cauchy sequence in ρ, there exists $N_k \in \boldsymbol{\omega}$ such that $N_k < N_{k+1}$ and $\rho(u_k(N_k), u_k(n)) < 1/(k+1)$ whenever $N_k \leq n \in \boldsymbol{\omega}$. Let $x(k) = u_k(N_k)$. Then $x \in T$, that is, x is a Cauchy sequence in ρ, because for any $r > 0$ there exists $K \in \boldsymbol{\omega}$ such that, for $K \leq k \in \boldsymbol{\omega}$, $d(u_K, u_k) + 1/K + 1/k < r$ and for $n \in \boldsymbol{\omega}$:

$$\begin{aligned}\rho(x(K), x(k)) &= \rho(u_K(N_K), u_k(N_k)) \\ &\leq \rho(u_K(N_K), u_K(n)) + \rho(u_K(n), u_k(n)) + \rho(u_k(n), u_k(N_k)).\end{aligned}$$

Taking the limit as $n \to \infty$ we get

$$\rho(x(K), x(k)) \leq 1/K + d(u_K, u_k) + 1/k < r.$$

We now check that $\lim_k d(x, u_k) = 0$. Given $r > 0$, choose $K \in \boldsymbol{\omega}$ so that $\rho(x(n), x(k)) + 1/k < r$ whenever $n, k \in \boldsymbol{\omega}$, $n \geq K$ and $k \geq K$. Then for $K \leq k \in \boldsymbol{\omega}$, $K \leq n \in \boldsymbol{\omega}$ and $N_k \leq n$:

$$\begin{aligned}\rho(x(n), u_k(n)) &\leq \rho(x(n), x(k)) + \rho(x(k), u_k(n)) \\ &= \rho(x(n), x(k)) + \rho(u_k(N_k), u_k(n)) < r.\end{aligned}$$

Taking the limit as $n \to \infty$ we get $d(x, u_k) \leq r$.

If we identify any $p \in S$ with the constant sequence $x \in T$ such that $x_n = p$ for every $n \in \boldsymbol{\omega}$, that is, if we replace the constant sequences by elements of S, we get the first part of our theorem. Suppose now that ρ is a metric. As in exercise 4.4.1, for each $x \in T$, let $x^* = \{y \in T\colon d(x, y) = 0\}$, $T' = \{x^*\colon x \in T\}$ and $d'(x^*, y^*) = d(x, y)$. Note that if x converges to p and y converges to q, then $d(x, y) = \rho(p, q)$ so that $p = q$ iff $d(x, y) = 0$, that is, $x^* = y^*$. We may therefore identify each point in S with the class of sequences converging to it. Thus, for each $p \in S$, let $p^* = \{x \in T\colon x \text{ converges to } p\}$, $S^* = \{p^*; p \in S\}$,

$$S' = S \cup (T' \sim S^*)$$

and

$$\rho'(p, q) = \begin{cases} d'(p^*, q^*) = \rho(p, q) & \text{if } p, q \in S \\ d'(p^*, q) & \text{if } p \in S, q \in T' \\ d'(p, q) & \text{if } p, q \in T'. \end{cases}$$

Since d' is a metric, so is ρ'. Since d is complete, we easily see the same is true of d' and hence of ρ'. It is also clear that S is dense in ρ'. ∎

7.6. Exercises

1. For $1 \leq p \leq \infty$, ℓ_p is complete in the metric induced by the ℓ_p-norm.
2. **C**([0; 1]) is complete in the metric induced by the sup norm (*Hint:* the uniform limit of continuous functions is continuous).

3. The Cantor set A on the line is defined by:

$$A = \left\{ \sum_{n \in \omega} \frac{x_n}{3^{n+1}} ; x \in \{0, 2\}^{\omega} \right\}.$$

Geometrically, it is obtained by starting with $[0; 1]$ and then successively throwing out the open middle third of each of the intervals one has left at each stage. Show that A is perfect and uncountable.

4. Let ρ be a complete metric on S, $0 < K < 1$ and f be a function on S to S such that $\rho(f(x), f(y)) \leq K\rho(x, y)$ for every $x, y \in S$. Show that there exists $x \in S$ with $f(x) = x$.
(*Hint:* let $t_0 \in S$ and $t_{n+1} = f(t_n)$ for $n \in \omega$).

8. COMPACTNESS

An amazingly large number of the properties of $[0; 1]$, especially those connected with continuous functions, can be derived directly from the Heine-Borel theorem (see 8.6.1). Hence sets for which the conclusion of the theorem holds have been isolated and extensively studied. They are called compact. Unlike completeness however, the definition of compactness is valid in any topological space and in such spaces it is frequently used as a substitute for completeness in hypotheses of theorems.

8.1. Definition
For any topology $\mathscr{G}$ on a space S and $A \subset S$:

$\mathscr{G}$ is compact iff every open covering in $\mathscr{G}$ has a finite subcovering. A is compact in $\mathscr{G}$ iff the restriction of $\mathscr{G}$ to A is compact (that is, every family of open sets which covers A has a finite subfamily which also covers A).

Another characterization and some properties of compactness are given in the following theorems.

8.2. Theorem. For any topology on S, S is compact iff every family F of closed sets with $\bigcap F = \phi$ has a finite subfamily F' with $\bigcap F' = \phi$.

■ **proof:** The theorem follows immediately from the fact that if F and G are any two families of subsets of S such that $A \in F$ iff $S \sim A \in G$, then $\bigcap F = S \sim \bigcup G$ so that $\bigcap F = \phi$ iff G covers S and F is finite iff G is finite. ■

8.3. Theorems. Let $\mathscr{G}$ be any topology on S and A be compact in $\mathscr{G}$. Then:
(1) For every infinite $B \subset A$ there exists $x \in A$ such that, for every $U \in \text{nbhd } x$, $B \cap U$ is infinite.

(2) If B is closed, then $B \cap A$ is compact.
(3) If $\mathcal{G}$ is Hausdorff, B is compact, and $A \cap B = \phi$, then there exist $A', B' \in \mathcal{G}$ such that $A \subset A'$, $B \subset B'$, and $A' \cap B' = \phi$.
(4) If $\mathcal{G}$ is Hausdorff, then A is closed.

■ **proofs**

(1) Let B be infinite and $B \subset A$. If, for every $x \in A$, there exists $U_x \in \text{nbhd } x$ such that $B \cap U_x$ is finite, then, since a finite number of the U_x cover A, B would have to be finite contradicting the assumption that B is infinite.
(2) Let B be closed and F a family of open sets covering $B \cap A$. If $F' = F \cup \{S \sim B\}$, then F' is an open cover of A and hence F' has a finite subfamily which covers A. Since $S \sim B$ covers no portion of $B \cap A$, a finite subfamily of F must cover $B \cap A$.
(3) Suppose $\mathcal{G}$ is Hausdorff, B is compact, and $A \cap B = \phi$. First, for each $x \in A$ we shall find U_x, $V_x \in \mathcal{G}$ so that $x \in U_x$, $B \subset V_x$, and $U_x \cap V_x = \phi$. To this end, let $x \in A$ and, for each $y \in B$, let M_y, $N_y \in \mathcal{G}$, $x \in M_y$, $y \in N_y$, and $M_y \cap N_y = \phi$. Since B is compact, a finite number of the N_y cover B so let β be finite, $\beta \subset B$ and $B \subset \bigcup_{y \in \beta} N_y$. If $U_x = \bigcap_{y \in \beta} M_y$ and $V_x = \bigcup_{y \in \beta} N_y$ then U_x, $V_x \in \mathcal{G}$, $x \in U_x$, $B \subset V_x$, and $U_x \cap V_x \subset \bigcup_{y \in \beta} (M_y \cap N_y) = \phi$. Now, since A is compact, a finite number of the U_x cover A so let α be finite, $\alpha \subset A$ and $A \subset \bigcup_{x \in \alpha} U_x$. If $A' = \bigcup_{x \in \alpha} U_x$ and $B' = \bigcap_{x \in \alpha} V_x$, then $A', B' \in \mathcal{G}$, $A \subset A'$, $B \subset B'$, and $A' \cap B' \subset \bigcup_{x \in \alpha} (U_x \cap V_x) = \phi$.
(4) If $\mathcal{G}$ is Hausdorff and $x \notin A$ then, since $\{x\}$ is compact, by (3) there exists $U \in \text{nbhd } x$ with $U \cap A = \phi$ so that $x \notin \text{closure } A$. Thus, $A = \text{closure } A$ and A is closed. ■

8.4. Theorems. Let $\mathcal{G}$ be a compact topology on S.
(1) If $\mathcal{G}$ is Hausdorff, then $\mathcal{G}$ is regular.
(2) If $\mathcal{G}$ is regular, then $\mathcal{G}$ is normal.

■ **proofs**

(1) This follows immediately from 8.3.2 and 8.3.3.
(2) Let A and B be closed, $A \cap B = \phi$. By 8.3.2 A and B are compact. If $\mathcal{G}$ is regular, then for every $x \in A$ there exist open U_x, V_x such that $x \in U_x$, $B \subset V_x$, and $U_x \cap V_x = \phi$. As in the proof of 8.3.3, a finite number of the U_x cover A, so let α be finite, $\alpha \subset A$ and $A \subset \bigcup_{x \in \alpha} U_x$. If $A' = \bigcup_{x \in \alpha} U_x$ and $B' = \bigcap_{x \in \alpha} V_x$ then A' and B' are open, $A \subset A'$, $B \subset B'$, and $A' \cap B' = \phi$. ■

We consider next properties of compactness in pseudometric spaces.

8.5. Theorem. For any pseudometric space S and $A \subset S$, the following three conditions are equivalent:
(a) A is compact,

(b) every sequence in A has a subsequence which converges to some point in A,

(c) A is totally bounded and complete.

■ **proof:** We show that (a) $\Rightarrow$ (b) $\Rightarrow$ (c) $\Rightarrow$ (a).
(a) $\Rightarrow$ (b): Let x be a sequence in A. If, for every $l \in A$, l is not a limit point of x then there exist $U_l \in$ nbhd l and $N_l \in \boldsymbol{\omega}$ such that $x_n \notin U_l$ whenever $N_l < n \in \boldsymbol{\omega}$. Since A is compact, a finite number of the U_l cover A so that, if K is the largest of the corresponding N_l, then $x_n \notin A$ for $n > K$ contradicting the fact that $x_n \in A$ for every $n \in \boldsymbol{\omega}$. Thus, x has a limit point $l \in A$ and, by 5.4.2, x has a subsequence which converges to l.
(b) $\Rightarrow$ (c): Clearly (b) implies that A is complete. If, for some $r > 0$, no finite number of spheres of radius r cover A then, if ρ is the pseudometric on S, by recursion we can form a sequence x in A with $\rho(x_m, x_n) \geq r$ for $m, n \in \boldsymbol{\omega}$, $m \neq n$ so that x cannot have any limit point. Thus, (b) implies that A is totally bounded.
(c) $\Rightarrow$ (a): Let F be a family of open sets covering A and suppose no finite subfamily of F covers A. Since A is totally bounded, a finite number of spheres of radius 1 cover A and therefore the portion of A lying in one of them, $A \cap \mathbf{S}(1, x_0)$, for some $x_0 \in S$, cannot be covered by any finite subfamily of F. Since any subset of a totally bounded set is totally bounded, by recursion we find, for each $n \in \boldsymbol{\omega}$, $B_n \subset A$ so that $B_{n+1} \subset B_n$, $\lim_n \operatorname{diam} B_n = 0$ and B_n cannot be covered by a finite subfamily of F. Since A is complete, if $x_n \in B_n$ for $n \in \boldsymbol{\omega}$, then x is a Cauchy sequence in A and hence converges to some $y \in A$. Now, for some $U \in F$, $y \in U$ and, for some $r > 0$, $\mathbf{S}(r, y) \subset U$ and, for large n, $\rho(x_n, y) < r/2$ and diam $B_n < r/2$ so that $B_n \subset \mathbf{S}(r, y) \subset U$, contradicting the fact that B_n could not be covered a finite subfamily of F. Thus, (c) implies that a finite subfamily of F covers A. ■

8.6. Exercises

1. In the standard topology on $\mathscr{R}^n$, for $n \in \boldsymbol{\omega}$, A is compact iff A is bounded and closed.
2. For $1 \leq p \leq \infty$, $\{x \in \ell_p: \|x\|_p \leq 1\}$ is not compact in the ℓ_p-norm.
3. $\{f \in \mathbf{C}([0; 1]): \|f\|_\infty \leq 1\}$ is not compact in the sup norm.
4. Let S be a pseudometric space and $A \subset S$. Then closure A is compact iff every sequence in A has a subsequence which converges to some point in S.
5. Let $\mathscr{G}$ be any topology on S and F be a nonempty family of nonempty compact sets such that, for every A, $B \in F$, either $A \subset B$ or $B \subset A$. If U is open and $\bigcap F \subset U$ then, for some $A \in F$, $A \subset U$.

9. BAIRE CATEGORY

A standard argument for showing that a certain set is not empty involves proving that, in some sense, its complement does not amount to very much.

For example, we use such an argument to show that irrational or transcendental numbers exist. In this case, we show that the rational or algebraic numbers, being countable, cannot exhaust the real line. Thus, measures of how thin or thick a given set is can be very useful. One such measure is the notion of Baire category. It turns out to have a great many applications and is instrumental in proving some very deep results.

9.1. Definitions

Let $\mathscr{G}$ be any topology on S and $A \subset S$.

(1) A is nowhere dense in $\mathscr{G}$ iff, for every nonempty $U \in \mathscr{G}$, $U \sim$ closure A in $\mathscr{G} \neq \phi$.
(2) A is of the first category in $\mathscr{G}$ iff there exists a sequence E such that, for every $n \in \boldsymbol{\omega}$, E_n is nowhere dense in $\mathscr{G}$ and $A = \bigcup_{n\in\omega} E_n$.
(3) A is of the second category in $\mathscr{G}$ iff A is not of the first category in $\mathscr{G}$.

The following theorem is the fundamental result about Baire category. Applications are mentioned in the exercises.

9.2. Theorem. In a topology which is either regular and compact or is induced by a complete pseudometric, every nonempty open set is of the second category.

■ **proof:** Suppose the topology is induced by a complete pseudometric on S, U is a nonempty open set and E is a sequence of nowhere dense sets. We show that $U \sim \bigcup_{n\in\omega} E_n \neq \phi$. Since $U \sim$ closure $E_0 \neq \phi$ and a pseudometric topology is regular, let B_0 be open, diam $B_0 < 1$ and $\phi \neq B_0 \subset$ closure $B_0 \subset U \sim$ closure E_0. Since $B_0 \sim$ closure $E_1 \neq \phi$, let B_1 be open, diam $B_1 < \frac{1}{2}$ and $\phi \neq B_1 \subset$ closure $B_1 \subset B_0 \sim$ closure E_1. Proceeding by recursion, for each $n \in \boldsymbol{\omega}$, let B_n be open, diam $B_n < 1/(n+1)$ and $\phi \neq B_{n+1} \subset$ closure $B_{n+1} \subset B_n \sim$ closure E_{n+1}. Since S is complete, we have by 7.2,

$$\phi \neq \bigcap_{n\in\omega} \text{closure } B_n \subset \bigcap_{n\in\omega} (U \sim E_n) = U \sim \bigcup_{n\in\omega} E_n.$$

If the topology is regular and compact, consider similar B_n without any reference to diameter and apply 8.2 instead of 7.2 to get the same conclusion. ■

The following lemmas follow immediately from the definitions.

9.3. Lemmas. In any topology:
(1) If A and B are nowhere dense, then $A \cup B$ is nowhere dense.
(2) If A is a sequence of sets of the first category, then $\bigcup_{n\in\omega} A_n$ is of the first category.
(3) If A is of the first category and $B \subset A$, then B is of the first category.

As corollaries of 9.2 we then have the following theorems.

9.4. Theorems. In a topology which is either regular and compact or is induced by a complete pseudometric on S:

(1) If U is open, $U \neq \phi$ and A is of the first category, then $U \sim A$ is of the second category.

(2) If U is open, $U \neq \phi$, and, for every $n \in \boldsymbol{\omega}$, $S \sim A_n$ is of the first category, then $\bigcap_{n \in \omega} (U \cap A_n)$ is of the second category.

(3) If, for every $n \in \boldsymbol{\omega}$, U_n is open and dense and $S \neq \phi$, then $\bigcap_{n \in \omega} U_n$ is of the second category.

■ **proofs**

(1) If $U \sim A$ is of the first category, then, since $U = (U \sim A) \cup (U \cap A)$, by 9.3, U would be of the first category too, contradicting 9.2.

(2) By 9.3, $\bigcup_{n \in \omega} (S \sim A_n) = S \sim \bigcap_{n \in \omega} A_n$ is of the first category hence, by (1), $U \sim (S \sim \bigcap_{n \in \omega} A_n) = \bigcap_{n \in \omega} (U \cap A_n)$ is of the second category.

(3) Since U_n is open and dense, $S \sim U_n$ is nowhere dense, hence

$$\bigcup_{n \in \omega} (S \sim U_n) = S \sim \bigcap_{n \in \omega} U_n$$

is of the first category and, by (1), its complement $\bigcap_{n \in \omega} U_n$ is of the second category. ■

9.5. Exercises

1. In the plane, the set of points with rational coordinates cannot be expressed as the intersection of a countable family of open sets.
2. Let $S = \mathbf{C}([0; 1])$ and $\mathscr{G}$ be the topology on S induced by the sup norm. For $K > 0$ and $\delta > 0$, let

$$M(K, \delta) = \{x \in S\colon \text{ there exists } t \in [0; 1] \text{ such that } |x(t) - x(t')| \leq K \cdot |t - t'| \text{ for every } t' \in [0; 1] \text{ with } |t - t'| < \delta\}.$$

Show that $M(K, \delta)$ is nowhere dense and hence that $\{x \in S\colon x$ is differentiable at some point in $[0; 1]\}$ is of the first category in $\mathscr{G}$. Thus, since S is complete, most continuous functions are not differentiable at any point.

3. Let $f_n \in \mathbf{C}(\mathscr{R})$ for $n \in \boldsymbol{\omega}$ and suppose that, for every $x \in \mathscr{R}$, $g(x) = \lim_n f_n(x) \in \mathscr{R}$. Show that $\{x \in \mathscr{R}\colon g$ is not continuous at $x\}$ is of the first category in the standard topology on $\mathscr{R}$.
4. Let $f \in \mathbf{C}(\mathscr{R})$ and its derivative f' be defined everywhere on $\mathscr{R}$. Show that $\{x \in \mathscr{R}\colon f'$ is not continuous at $x\}$ is of the first category in the standard topology on $\mathscr{R}$.

10. CONNECTEDNESS

If we consider sets in the plane, we see that there is more than one possible way of defining connectedness. From a combinatorial point of view, a set is connected if any two of its points can be joined by a curve lying entirely in the set. From a more purely set-theoretic point of view, a set is connected if it cannot be broken up into two well separated pieces. These two concepts do not agree in general. In this section we define connectedness from the second approach and in the exercises indicate relations to the other.

10.1. Definition

Let $\mathscr{G}$ be any topology on S and $A \subset S$.

$\mathscr{G}$ is connected iff there do not exist two disjoint, nonempty open sets in $\mathscr{G}$ which cover S.

A is connected in $\mathscr{G}$ iff $\mathscr{G}$ restricted to A is connected, that is, there do not exist $U, V \in \mathscr{G}$ such that

(a) $A \cap U \neq \phi$ and $A \cap V \neq \phi$,

(b) $A \cap U \cap V = \phi$,

(c) $A \subset U \cup V$.

10.2. Theorems. In any topology:

(1) If F is a family of connected sets and $\bigcap F \neq \phi$, then $\bigcup F$ is connected.

(2) If A is connected, then closure A is connected.

■ **proofs**

(1) Let $A = \bigcup F$ and $x \in \bigcap F$. If A is not connected, then there exist open U, V satisfying conditions (a), (b), (c) of definition 10.1 above. Suppose $x \in U$. Since $V \cap A \neq \phi$, there exists $\alpha \in F$ with $V \cap \alpha \neq \phi$. Since $x \in \alpha$, we have $U \cap \alpha \neq \phi$ also, so that α is not connected.

(2) Let A be connected and $\bar{A} =$ closure A. If $\bar{A}$ is not connected, let U, V be open, $\bar{A} \cap U \neq \phi$, $\bar{A} \cap V \neq \phi$, $\bar{A} \cap U \cap V = \phi$, and $\bar{A} \subset U \cup V$. Since A is connected, we must have $A \cap U = \phi$ or $A \cap V = \phi$. Suppose $A \cap V = \phi$. Then $A \subset S \sim V$ and, since $S \sim V$ is closed, $\bar{A} \subset S \sim V$, that is, $\bar{A} \cap V = \phi$ in contradiction to $\bar{A} \cap V \neq \phi$. ■

As a consequence of the above theorems, any topological space can be broken up into a disjoint family of connected and closed pieces called components.

10.3. Definition

For any topology $\mathscr{G}$ on S and $x \in S$:

component x in $\mathscr{G} = \bigcup\{A\colon A$ is connected in $\mathscr{G}$ and $x \in A\}$.

10.4. Theorems. For any topology on S and $x, y \in S$:

(1) component x is connected and closed.

(2) component $x \cap$ component $y \neq \phi$ iff component $x =$ component y

(3) If every point in S has a connected neighborhood, then component x is also open.

■ **proofs**

(1) This follows immediately from 10.2.

(2) Let A = component x and B = component y. If $A \cap B \neq \phi$ then, by 10.2.1, $A \cup B$ is connected and $\{x, y\} \subset A \cup B$; hence $A \cup B \subset A$ and $A \cup B \subset B$, that is, $A = A \cup B = B$.

(3) Let A = component x. If $y \in A$ and $U \in$ nbhd y and U is connected, then, by 10.2.1, $A \cup U$ is connected, hence $A \cup U = A$ and therefore $U \subset A$. Thus, if every $y \in A$ has a connected neighborhood then A is open. ■

10.5. Exercises

1. In the standard topology for $\mathscr{R}$, A is connected iff A is an interval, that is, for every $x, y \in A$, $[x; y] \subset A$. Hence any open set is the union of a countable family of disjoint open intervals.
2. Let A be open in the standard topology for $\mathscr{R}^2$. Then A is connected iff any two points in A can be joined by a polygonal path lying entirely in A.
3. Let $A = \{(x, y): x > 0 \text{ and } y = \sin(1/x)\}$. In the standard topology for $\mathscr{R}^2$, A is connected hence so is its closure, $\bar{A}$. Show that $\bar{A} = A \cup (\{0\} \times [-1; 1])$, but that no continuous curve lying in $\bar{A}$ can join any point in A with $(0, 0)$.

11. MISCELLANEOUS EXERCISES

(1) Let $S = \omega^\omega$ and, for $x, y \in S$, let $N(x, y) = \inf\{n \in \omega: x_n \neq y_n\}$ and $\rho(x, y) = 1/(1 + N(x, y))$. Then ρ is a metric on S and
  (a) S is complete,
  (b) S is separable,
  (c) S is perfect,
  (d) S is not connected, in fact, for every $x \in S$, component $x = \{x\}$ so that x has no connected neighborhood.

(2) Let $S = [0; 1]^\omega$ and, for $x, y \in S$, let

$$\rho(x, y) = \sum_{n \in \omega} (1/2^n)\, |x_n - y_n|.$$

Then ρ is a metric and S is compact.

(3) Let ρ be a metric on S and for $A \subset S$, $A \neq \phi$ and $t > 0$, let $A^*(t) = \{x \in S: \text{dist}(\{x\}, A) < t\}$. Let $S' = \{A: A \subset S, A \neq \phi\}$ and, for $A, B \in S'$ let $\rho'(A, B) = \inf\{t: A \subset B^*(t) \text{ and } B \subset A^*(t)\}$. Then ρ' is a pseudometric on S' and
  (a) for any $A \in S'$, closure A is the only closed set in $\{B \in S': \rho'(A, B) = 0\}$. Thus, the restriction of ρ' to the family of closed sets is a metric.

(b) If S is compact in ρ, then S' is compact in ρ'.

(*Hint:* If A is any sequence in S', find a Cauchy subsequence B of A and show that B converges to $\bigcap_{N\in\omega}$ closure $\bigcup_{n\geqq N} B_n$.)

(4) In any pseudometric space, every closed set is the intersection of a countable family of open sets.

(5) Let A and B be nonempty, disjoint subsets of a metric space. Must dist $(A, B) > 0$? What if they are both closed or both compact or one is closed and the other compact?

4. CONTINUOUS FUNCTIONS

1. INTRODUCTION

Since continuity is based only on the notion of neighborhood or convergence, it can be readily defined for functions mapping any topological space into another. In this chapter, after introducing the concept, we develop some of its fundamental properties. One major interest is to determine conditions under which the limit of continuous functions is continuous. This leads us to uniform convergence and equicontinuity. Also, when we deal with vector spaces, the continuous linear functions play a very important role. For this reason, we devote a section to these functions.

2. CONTINUITY AND LIMITS

The definitions of continuity and limit given below follow the usual approach found in calculus texts. As can be seen from theorem 2.3.3, continuity can also be formulated much more simply and elegantly in set-theoretic terms. For this reason, the set-theoretic formulation (2.3.3.(a)) is used in more sophisticated approaches. An added advantage of this formulation is that it leads very naturally to other classes of functions, for instance, measurable functions, Borel functions (see Chapter 7).

2.1. Definitions

Let $\mathscr{G}$ and $\mathscr{G}'$ be topologies on S and S' respectively and f be a function.

(1) f is continuous at x in $(\mathscr{G}, \mathscr{G}')$ iff $x \in S \cap \text{domain} f$, $f(x) \in S'$ and, for every $V \in \text{nbhd} f(x)$ in $\mathscr{G}'$, there exists $U \in \text{nbhd}\ x$ in $\mathscr{G}$ with $f[U] \subset V$, that is, $f^{-1}[V] \in \text{nbhd}\ x$ in $\mathscr{G}$.

(2) f is continuous in $(\mathscr{G}, \mathscr{G}')$ iff, for every $x \in \text{domain} f$, f is continuous at x in $(\mathscr{G}, \mathscr{G}')$.

(3) f is continuous on A in $(\mathscr{G}, \mathscr{G}')$ iff $A \subset \text{domain} f$ and $f|A$ is continuous in $(\mathscr{G}, \mathscr{G}')$.

Note that, for any $U, f[U] = f[U \cap \text{domain} f]$ so that for f to be continuous, its domain need not be the whole space and its behavior at isolated points of its domain is immaterial (for example, if domain $f = [0; 1] \cup [2; 3]$, $f(x) = 0$ for $x \in [0; 1]$ and $f(x) = 1$ for $x \in [2; 3]$, then f is continuous). However, we must have domain $f \subset S$ and range $f \subset S'$.

The closely related concept of limit is introduced next.

2.2. Definitions

Let $\mathscr{G}$ and $\mathscr{G}'$ be topologies on S and S' respectively and f be a function.

(1) $y \doteq \text{limit}_{t \to x} f(t)$ in $(\mathscr{G}, \mathscr{G}')$ iff $x \in S$, $y \in S'$ and, for every $V \in \text{nbhd}\ y$ in $\mathscr{G}'$, there exists $U \in \text{nbhd}\ x$ in $\mathscr{G}$ with $f[U - \{x\}] \subset V$.

(2) $y \doteq \text{limit}_{t \to x} f(t)$ on A in $(\mathscr{G}, \mathscr{G}')$ iff $y \doteq \text{limit}_{t \to x} (f|A)(t)$ in $(\mathscr{G}, \mathscr{G}')$.

When the y satisfying the above definitions is unique, we may replace $\doteq$ by $=$.

Note that, in definition 2.2.1 above, x need not belong to domain f and if x is not an accumulation point of $(S \cap \text{domain} f)$, then any $y \in S'$ satisfies the definition. This fact is useful in characterizing continuity in terms of limits at isolated points.

The following characterizations of continuity follow readily from the definitions and their proofs are left as exercises.

2.3. Theorems. Let $\mathscr{G}$ and $\mathscr{G}'$ be topologies on S and S' and f be a function. Then:

(1) f is continuous at x in $(\mathscr{G}, \mathscr{G}')$ iff $f(x) \doteq \text{limit}_{t \to x} f(t)$ in $(\mathscr{G}, \mathscr{G}')$.

(2) f is continuous on A in $(\mathscr{G}, \mathscr{G}')$ iff $A \subset S \cap \text{domain} f$, $f[A] \subset S'$ and $f|A$ is continuous in (restriction of $\mathscr{G}$ to A, restriction of $\mathscr{G}'$ to $f[A]$).

(3) If f is on S to S', then f is continuous in $(\mathscr{G}, \mathscr{G}')$ iff any one of the following conditions holds:
  (a) for every $V \in \mathscr{G}', f^{-1}[V] \in \mathscr{G}$,
  (b) for every $C \subset S'$, if C is closed in $\mathscr{G}'$, then $f^{-1}[C]$ is closed in $\mathscr{G}$,
  (c) for every $A \subset S, f[\text{closure}\ A \text{ in } \mathscr{G}] \subset \text{closure}\ f[A]$ in $\mathscr{G}'$.

We list next some of the fundamental properties of continuous functions.

2.4. Theorems. Let $\mathscr{G}$ and $\mathscr{G}'$ be any topologies on S and S', respectively, $A \subset S$ and f be continuous on A in $(\mathscr{G}, \mathscr{G}')$.

(1) If A is compact in $\mathscr{G}$, then $f[A]$ is compact in $\mathscr{G}'$.

(2) If A is Lindelöf in $\mathscr{G}$, then $f[A]$ is Lindelöf in $\mathscr{G}'$.

(3) If A is connected in $\mathscr{G}$, then $f[A]$ is connected in $\mathscr{G}'$.

■ **proof:** If F' is an open covering in the restriction of $\mathscr{G}'$ to $f[A]$, let $F = \{A \cap f^{-1}[V];\ V \in F'\}$. Then F is an open covering in the restriction of $\mathscr{G}$ to A. If a finite (or countable) subfamily of F covers A, then the corresponding subfamily of F' is finite (or countable) and covers $f[A]$. If F' consists of two disjoint nonempty sets, then the same is true of F. ■

2.5. Theorem. If f is continuous on A in $(\mathscr{G}, \mathscr{G}')$ and g is continuous on $f[A]$ in $(\mathscr{G}', \mathscr{G}'')$, then $g \circ f$ is continuous on A in $(\mathscr{G}, \mathscr{G}'')$.

■ **proof:** Immediate from 2.3. ■

2.6. Exercises

1. A continuous function on $[0; 1]$ to $\mathscr{R}$ assumes a maximum, minimum, and every value in between.
2. Let A be a nonempty subset of a metric space S and, for every $x \in S$, $f(x) = \text{dist}(\{x\}, A)$. Then f is continuous on S.
3. Let A and B be nonempty, disjoint, closed subsets of a metric space S. Then there exists a continuous function f on S to $[0; 1]$ such that $f(x) = 0$ for $x \in A$ and $f(x) = 1$ for $x \in B$.
4. (Tietze's Theorem). Let A be a closed subset of a metric space S and f a continuous function on A to $[0; 1]$. Then there exists a continuous function g on S to $[0; 1]$ such that $g(x) = f(x)$ for $x \in A$.
5. Let S be a metric space and f be any function on S to $\mathscr{R}$. Then $\{x \in S : f \text{ is continuous at } x\}$ can be expressed as the intersection of a countable family of open sets. ■

3. UNIFORM CONTINUITY

In case both the domain and range of a function are pseudometric spaces, we can introduce in an obvious way the notion of uniform continuity on a set.

3.1. Definition

Let ρ and ρ' be pseudometrics on S and S' respectively and f be a function.

(1) f is uniformly continuous on A in (ρ, ρ') iff $A \subset S \cap \text{domain} f$ and, for every $r' > 0$, there exists $r > 0$ such that, for every $x, y \in A$, if $\rho(x, y) < r$, then $\rho'(f(x), f(y)) < r'$.

(2) f is uniformly continuous in (ρ, ρ') iff f is uniformly continuous on domain f in (ρ, ρ').

3.2. Theorem. For any pseudometrics ρ and ρ', if f is continuous on A in (ρ, ρ') and A is compact in ρ, then f is uniformly continuous on A in (ρ, ρ').

■ **proof:** Suppose f is not uniformly continuous on A. Then there exist $r' > 0$ and $x_n, y_n \in A$ for every $n \in \boldsymbol{\omega}$ so that $\rho(x_n, y_n) < 1/(n + 1)$ and $\rho'(f(x_n), f(y_n)) > r'$. Since A is compact, let $l \in A$ be a limit point of the sequence x. Since f is continuous on A, choose $r > 0$ so that, for every $a \in A$, if $\rho(l, a) < r$ then $\rho'(f(l), f(a)) < r'/2$. Then there exists $n \in \boldsymbol{\omega}$ so that $1/(n+1) < r/2$ and $\rho(l, x_n) < r/2$, hence

$$\rho(l, y_n) \leq \rho(l, x_n) + \rho(x_n, y_n) < r$$

and $$\rho'(f(x_n), f(y_n)) \leq \rho'(f(x_n), f(l)) + \rho'(f(l), f(y_n)) < r',$$

contradicting the choice of r', x_n and y_n. ∎

3.3. Exercises

1. Let S be a metric space, $A \subset S$ and f be a uniformly continuous function on A to $\mathscr{R}$. Then f can be extended to a continuous function on closure A to $\mathscr{R}$.
2. Let S be a compact metric space, $A \subset S$, and f be a uniformly continuous function on A to $\mathscr{R}$. Then $f[A]$ is bounded.

4. HOMEOMORPHISMS

For counting purposes, two sets are identified if they can be put in a one-to-one correspondence with each other. For topological purposes, we require in addition that the correspondence preserve the topologies, that is, map open sets into open sets both ways.

4.1. Definitions

Let $\mathscr{G}$ and $\mathscr{G}'$ be topologies on S and S' respectively.

(1) f is a homeomorphism in $(\mathscr{G}, \mathscr{G}')$ iff f is a one-to-one function, f is continuous in $(\mathscr{G}, \mathscr{G}')$ and f^{-1} is continuous in $(\mathscr{G}', \mathscr{G})$.

(2) f is a homeomorphism on A in $(\mathscr{G}, \mathscr{G}')$ iff $A \subset$ domain f and f/A is a homeomorphism in $(\mathscr{G}, \mathscr{G}')$.

(3) f is a homeomorphism on A to B in $(\mathscr{G}, \mathscr{G}')$ iff f is a homeomorphism on A in $(\mathscr{G}, \mathscr{G}')$ and $f[A] \subset B$.

(4) f is a homeomorphism on A onto B in $(\mathscr{G}, \mathscr{G}')$ iff f is a homeomorphism on A in $(\mathscr{G}, \mathscr{G}')$ and $f[A] = B$.

(5) A is homeomorphic to B in $(\mathscr{G}, \mathscr{G}')$ iff there exists a homeomorphism on A onto B in $(\mathscr{G}, \mathscr{G}')$.

(6) $\mathscr{G}$ is homeomorphic to $\mathscr{G}'$ iff S is homeomorphic to S' in $(\mathscr{G}, \mathscr{G}')$.

The following characterizations of homeomorphism are immediate from the definitions and theorems 2.3.

4.2. Theorem. For any topologies $\mathscr{G}$ and $\mathscr{G}'$ on S and S' respectively, f is a homeomorphism on S onto S' in $(\mathscr{G}, \mathscr{G}')$ iff f is one-to-one on S onto S' and any one of the following conditions holds:

(a) for every $U \in \mathscr{G}$ and $V \in \mathscr{G}'$, $f[U] \in \mathscr{G}'$ and $f^{-1}[V] \in \mathscr{G}$.

(b) f is continuous in $(\mathscr{G}, \mathscr{G}')$ and $f[A]$ is closed in $\mathscr{G}'$ whenever A is closed in $\mathscr{G}$.

(c) for every $A \subset S$, f[closure A in $\mathscr{G}$] $=$ closure $f[A]$ in $\mathscr{G}'$.

The following theorem gives a very useful criterion for checking that a continuous function is a homeomorphism.

4.3. Theorem. Let $\mathscr{G}$ be a compact topology on S and $\mathscr{G}'$ be a Hausdorff topology on S'. If f is one-to-one and continuous on S in $(\mathscr{G}, \mathscr{G}')$, then f is a homeomorphism in $(\mathscr{G}, \mathscr{G}')$.

■ **proof:** If A is closed in $\mathscr{G}$, then A is compact in $\mathscr{G}$; hence $f[A]$ is compact in $\mathscr{G}'$ and, since $\mathscr{G}'$ is Hausdorff, $f[A]$ is closed in $\mathscr{G}'$. ■

4.4. Exercises

1. Show that $[0; 1]$ is not homeomorphic to $[0; 1] \times [0; 1]$.
2. Show that $(0; 1)$ is homeomorphic to $\mathscr{R}$.

5. LIMITS OF FUNCTIONS AND EQUICONTINUITY

In this section we are primarily interested in discussing conditions under which the limit of continuous functions is continuous. We first note that there are two types of convergence for functions: ordinary or pointwise convergence and uniform convergence. These are introduced in the following definitions.

5.1. Definitions

Let S and S' be any spaces and $\mathscr{G}'$ be a topology on S'.

(1) For any sequence f of functions on S to S': f converges pointwise to g in $\mathscr{G}'$ iff g is on S to S' and, for every $x \in S, f_n(x) \xrightarrow{n} g(x)$ in $\mathscr{G}'$.

(2) For any family F of functions on S to S': g is a pointwise limit of F in $\mathscr{G}'$ iff g is on S to S' and, for every finite $A \subset S$ and $U_x \in \text{nbhd } g(x)$ in $\mathscr{G}'$ for $x \in A$, there exists $f \in F$ with $f(x) \in U_x$ for $x \in A$.

5.2. Definitions

Let S and S' be any spaces and ρ' be a pseudometric on S'.

(1) For any sequence f of functions on S to S': f converges uniformly to g in ρ' iff g is on S to S' and $\lim_n \sup_{x \in S} \rho'(f_n(x), g(x)) = 0$.

(2) For any family F of functions on S to S': g is a uniform limit of F in ρ' iff g is on S to S' and, for every $r > 0$, there exists $f \in F$ with $\sup_{x \in S} \rho'(f(x), g(x)) < r$.

We should point out that the notion of pointwise and uniform convergence can be discussed in the context of Chapter 3 by introducing appropriate topologies on families of functions on S to S'. This has already been done in special cases of real valued functions (see exercise 3.4.4 in Chapter 3). The same ideas apply in the more general situations and are taken up in theorem 5.10 and exercise 5.11.3.

Next, we introduce the notion of equicontinuity which will be needed in the theorems later on.

5.3. Definitions

Let F be a family of functions on S to S', $\mathscr{G}$ be a topology on S and ρ' be a pseudometric on S'.

(1) F is equicontinuous at x in $(\mathscr{G}, \rho')$ iff $x \in S$ and, for every $r > 0$, there exists $U \in$ nbhd x in $\mathscr{G}$ such that, for every $y \in U$ and $f \in F$, $\rho'(f(x), f(y)) < r$.

(2) F is equicontinuous in $(\mathscr{G}, \rho')$ iff, for every $x \in S$, F is equicontinuous at x in $(\mathscr{G}, \rho')$.

Note that if F is finite, then F is equicontinuous iff every $f \in F$ is continuous. Thus, the condition is significant only when F is infinite.

The two best known general conditions under which limits of continuous functions are continuous are given in the next theorems.

5.4. Theorems. Let F be a family of functions on S to S', $\mathscr{G}$ be a topology on S, ρ' be a pseudometric on S' and $x \in S$.

(1) If every function in F is continuous at x in $(\mathscr{G}, \rho')$ and g is a uniform limit of F in ρ', then g is continuous at x in $(\mathscr{G}, \rho')$.

(2) If F is equicontinuous at x in $(\mathscr{G}, \rho')$ and g is a pointwise limit of F in ρ', then g is continuous at x in $(\mathscr{G}, \rho')$.

■ **proofs:** Given $V \in$ nbhd $g(x)$, let $r > 0$ and $\mathbf{S}(3r, g(x)) \subset V$.

(1) If g is a uniform limit of F and every function in F is continuous at x, choose $f \in F$ so that $\rho'(f(y), g(y)) < r$ for every $y \in S$ and then $U \in$ nbhd x so that $f[U] \subset \mathbf{S}(r, f(x))$. Then, for any $y \in U$,

$$\rho'(g(x), g(y)) \leq \rho'(g(x), f(x)) + \rho'(f(x), f(y)) + \rho'(f(y), g(y)) < 3r$$

so that $g[U] \subset \mathbf{S}(3r, g(x)) \subset V$.

(2) If F is equicontinuous at x, let $U \in$ nbhd x be such that $\rho'(f(y), f(x)) < r$ for every $y \in U$ and $f \in F$. If g is a pointwise limit of F, for any $y \in U$ there exists $f \in F$ such that $\rho'(f(y), g(y)) < r$ and $\rho'(f(x), g(x)) < r$; hence

$$\rho'(g(x), g(y)) \leq \rho'(g(x), f(x)) + \rho'(f(x), f(y)) + \rho'(f(y), g(y)) < 3r$$

so that $g[U] \subset \mathbf{S}(3r, g(x)) \subset V$. ■

We should note that the proof of 5.4.2 above gives in fact the following stronger result.

5.5. Theorem. Let F be a family of functions on S to S', $\mathscr{G}$ be a topology on S, ρ' be a pseudometric on S', and $F' = \{g : g \text{ is a pointwise limit of } F \text{ in } \rho'\}$. If $x \in S$ and F is equicontinuous at x in $(\mathscr{G}, \rho')$, then F' is equicontinuous at x in $(\mathscr{G}, \rho')$.

In case the topology on S is also induced by a pseudometric, we can introduce the notion of uniform equicontinuity.

5.6. Definition

For ρ and ρ' pseudometrics on S and S', respectively, and F a family of functions on S to S': F is uniformly equicontinuous in (ρ, ρ') iff, for every $r' > 0$ there exists $r > 0$ such that, for every $x, y \in S$ and $f \in F$, if $\rho(x, y) < r$, then $\rho'(f(x), f(y)) < r'$.

The following theorem is an immediate generalization of theorem 3.2. Since the proof is essentially the same as that of 3.2, it is left as an exercise.

5.7. Theorem. Let ρ and ρ' be pseudometrics on S and S', respectively, and F be a family of functions on S to S'. If S is compact in ρ and F is equicontinuous in (ρ, ρ'), then F is uniformly equicontinuous in (ρ, ρ').

We next give the fundamental theorem about equicontinuous families.

5.8. Theorem. Let ρ and ρ' be pseudometrics on S and S', respectively, and F be a family of functions on S to S'. If S is totally bounded in ρ, S' is compact in ρ', and F is uniformly equicontinuous in (ρ, ρ'), then every sequence in F has a subsequence which converges uniformly to a continuous function on S in (ρ, ρ').

■ **proof:** Let f bc a sequence in F. If S is totally bounded, then, for every $n \in \omega$, there exists a finite set $T_n \subset S$ such that for every $x \in S$ there is a $t \in T_n$ with $\rho(x, t) < 1/(n + 1)$. If S' is compact then there is a subsequence f^0 of f such that the $f_i^0(t)$ converge for $t \in T_0$. By recursion we can find f^n for $n \in \omega$ so that f^{n+1} is a subsequence of f^n and the $f_i^n(t)$ converge for $t \in T_n$. Let $g_n = f_n^n$ for $n \in \omega$. Then g is a subsequence of f and the $g_n(t)$ converge for $t \in \bigcup_{n\in\omega} T_n$. If F is uniformly equicontinuous then for any $r' > 0$, there exists $r > 0$ such that if $\rho(x, y) < r$ then $\rho'(g_n(x), g_n(y)) < r'$ for every $n \in \omega$. Let $N \in \omega$ with $1/(N + 1) < r$, then choose $K \in \omega$ so that for $m, n \in \omega$ with $m > K$ and $n > K$ we have $\rho'(g_m(t), g_n(t)) < r'$ for every $t \in T_N$. For such m, n and any $x \in S$ there exists a $t \in T_N$ with $\rho(x, t) < 1/(N + 1) < r$ and hence

$$\rho'(g_m(x), g_n(x)) \leq \rho'(g_m(x), g_m(t)) + \rho'(g_m(t), g_n(t)) + \rho'(g_n(t), g_n(x)) < 3r'.$$

Thus, the $g_n(x)$ form a Cauchy sequence in S' and therefore there exists $h(x) \in S'$ with $g_n(x) \xrightarrow{n} h(x)$. The convergence is uniform since, for $m > K$

$$\rho'(g_m(x), h(x)) \leq \lim_n \rho'(g_m(x), g_n(x)) + \rho'(g_n(x), h(x)) \leq 3r'$$

for every $x \in S$. Hence, by 5.4, h is continuous on S. ■

In view of 5.7, we have the following corollary of 5.8.

5.9. Theorem (Ascoli-Arzela). Let S and S' be compact pseudometric spaces and F be an equicontinuous family of functions on S to S'. Then every sequence in F has a subsequence which converges uniformly to a continuous function on S.

We can reformulate the above theorem, along with its converse, within the context of Chapter 3 by introducing a natural pseudometric in the space of continuous functions.

5.10. Theorems. Let $\mathscr{G}$ be a topology on S, ρ' be a pseudometric on S', $C = \{f: f \text{ is continuous on } S \text{ in } (\mathscr{G}, \rho')\}$ and for $f, g \in C$ let

$$d(f, g) = \sup_{x \in S} \rho'(f(x), g(x)).$$

(1) If $d(f, g) < \infty$ for every $f, g \in C$, then d is a pseudometric on C.
(2) If $d(f, g) < \infty$ for every $f, g \in C$, $F \subset C$ and F is compact in d, then F is equicontinuous in $(\mathscr{G}, \rho')$.
(3) If $\mathscr{G}$ is induced by a pseudometric ρ, S and S' are compact in ρ and ρ', respectively, and $F \subset C$ then:
F is equicontinuous in $(\mathscr{G}, \rho')$ iff closure F in d is compact in d.

■ **proofs**
(1) This is immediate from properties of sup.
(2) Suppose $F \subset C$ and F is compact in d. Given $x \in S$ and $r' > 0$, for every $U \in \text{nbhd } x$ in $\mathscr{G}$, let

$$H_U = \{f \in F: \rho'(f(x), f(y)) < r' \text{ for every } y \in U\},$$
$$G_U = \{g \in F: \text{for some } f \in H_U,\ d(f, g) < r'\}.$$

Then G_U is open in d and since F consists of continuous functions $\{G_U; U \in \text{nbhd } x\}$ covers F. Since F is compact in d, there exist $n \in \boldsymbol{\omega}$ and $U_0, \cdots, U_n \in \text{nbhd } x$ with $F = \bigcup_{i=0}^{n} G_{U_i}$. Let $V = \bigcap_{i=0}^{n} U_i$. If $y \in V$ and $g \in F$, then, for some $i = 0, \cdots, n$, $g \in G_{U_i}$ and, for some $f \in H_{U_i}$, $d(f, g) < r'$ so that

$$\rho'(g(x), g(y)) \leq \rho'(g(x), f(x)) + \rho'(f(x), f(y)) + \rho'(f(y), g(y)) < 3r'.$$

Thus, F is equicontinuous at x.
(3) Note that, by 5.5, F is equicontinuous iff closure F in d is equicontinuous. The desired result is then a consequence of (2) and theorem 5.9, using the characterization of compactness in terms of sequences given in theorem 8.5 of Chapter 3. ■

5.11. Exercises
1. Let f be a sequence of continuous functions on $[0; 1]$ to $\mathscr{R}$ such that $f_n(x) \leq f_{n+1}(x)$ for every $n \in \boldsymbol{\omega}$ and $x \in [0; 1]$. If f converges pointwise to h and h is continuous on $[0; 1]$, then f converges uniformly to h.
2. Let $0 < K < \infty$ and f be a sequence of differentiable functions on $\mathscr{R}$ to $\mathscr{R}$ such that $|f_n'(x)| < K$ and $|f_n(0)| < K$ for every $n \in \boldsymbol{\omega}$ and $x \in \mathscr{R}$.

Then there exists a subsequence g of f which converges pointwise to a continuous function on $\mathscr{R}$.

3. Let S and S' be any spaces, $\mathscr{G}'$ be a topology on S', and T be the set of all functions on S to S'. For each finite $A \subset S$ and function U on A to $\mathscr{G}'$, let

$$V(A, U) = \{f \in T: f(x) \in U_x \text{ for } x \in A\}.$$

Let $\mathscr{T}$ be the family of all $F \subset T$ such that for every $f \in F$ there exists a finite $A \subset S$ and function U on A to $\mathscr{G}'$ with $f \in V(A, U) \subset F$. Check that $\mathscr{T}$ is a topology on T, and that for any $F \subset T$, $f \in$ closure F in $\mathscr{T}$ iff $f \in T$ and f is a pointwise limit of F in $\mathscr{G}'$.

Note the geometric interpretation of the above sets: T is the Cartesian product of as many copies of S' as there are points in S, that is, $T = S'^S$ (see definition 2.1.4 in Chapter 2); $V(A, U)$ is a cylinder having as a base a rectangle formed by taking the Cartesian product of a finite number of open sets in $\mathscr{G}'$, one for each $x \in A$. For this reason, for any $F \subset T$, the restriction of $\mathscr{T}$ to F is referred to both as the topology of pointwise convergence and as the product topology on F.

6. LINEAR FUNCTIONALS

In the study of pseudonormed vector spaces, the family of continuous, real-valued linear functions plays a very important role. In this section we merely introduce such functions and mention some of their elementary properties.

6.1. Definitions

Let S be a vector space under $(+, \cdot, \ominus)$.

(1) φ is a linear functional on S iff φ is on S to $\mathscr{R}$ and, for every $x, y \in S$ and $a, b \in \mathscr{R}$:

$$\varphi(a \cdot x + b \cdot y) = a \cdot \varphi(x) + b \cdot \varphi(y).$$

(2) $S^* = \{\varphi: \varphi \text{ is a linear functional on } S\}$.

(3) For any topology $\mathscr{G}$ on S,

$$\mathscr{L}(\mathscr{G}) = \{\varphi \in S^*: \varphi \text{ is continuous in } \mathscr{G}\}.$$

The following elementary results are basic to all work with linear functionals.

6.2. Theorems. Let S be a vector space under $(+, \cdot, \ominus)$ and P be a pseudonorm on S. Then:

(1) For every $x, y \in S$ and $W \in \text{nbhd}\,(x + y)$ in P there exist $U \in \text{nbhd}\, x$ in P and $V \in \text{nbhd}\, y$ in P such that $x' + y' \in W$ whenever $x' \in U$ and $y' \in V$ (thus, $+$ is continuous as a function of two variables).

(2) For every $a \in \mathscr{R}$, $x \in S$ and $W \in \text{nbhd}\,(a \cdot x)$ in P there exists $r > 0$ and $U \in \text{nbhd}\, x$ in P such that $b \cdot y \in W$ whenever $|b - a| < r$ and $y \in U$. (Thus, $\cdot$ is continuous as a function of two variables.)

(3) $\varphi \in \mathscr{L}(P)$ iff $\varphi \in S^*$ and φ is continuous at $\ominus$ in P.
(4) $\varphi \in \mathscr{L}(P)$ iff there exists $M < \infty$ such that $|\varphi(x)| \leq M \cdot P(x)$ for every $x \in S$.

■ **proofs**
(1) This follows immediately from the fact that

$$P((x' + y') - (x + y)) \leq P(x' - x) + P(y' - y).$$

(2) Follows from the fact that:

$$P(b \cdot y - a \cdot x) = P(b \cdot y - b \cdot x + b \cdot x - a \cdot x)$$
$$\leq |b|\, P(y - x) + |b - a|\, P(x).$$

(3) Let $\varphi \in S^*$ and φ be continuous at $\ominus$. Given $x \in S$ and $r > 0$, let $U \in$ nbhd $\ominus$ be such that $|\varphi(z)| < r$ for $z \in U$. If $V = \{x + z; z \in U\}$, then $V \in$ nbhd x and, for $y \in V$ we have $y - x \in U$ so that

$$|\varphi(y) - \varphi(x)| = |\varphi(y - x)| < r.$$

(4) Let $\varphi \in \mathscr{L}(P)$. Since $\varphi(\ominus) = 0$ we must have $\varphi(x) = 0$ whenever $P(x) = 0$. If for every $n \in \boldsymbol{\omega}_+$ there exists $x_n \in S$ with $|\varphi(x_n)| > nP(x_n)$, let $y_n = (1/nP(x_n)) \cdot x_n$. Then $P(y_n) = 1/n$ so that $y_n \xrightarrow{n} \ominus$ but $|\varphi(y_n)| > 1$, contradicting the continuity of φ at $\ominus$. The converse is immediate using (3). ■

We should observe that under the usual operations for functions, both S^* and $\mathscr{L}(P)$ are vector spaces. They are known, respectively, as the algebraic and topological dual of S. In view of 6.2.4, we can introduce on $\mathscr{L}(P)$ a norm as follows.

6.3. Definition
For any pseudonorm P on a vector space S and $\varphi \in \mathscr{L}(P)$:

$$\|\varphi\|_P = \inf \{M: M > 0 \text{ and } |\varphi(x)| \leq MP(x) \text{ for every } x \in S\}.$$

We then have the following fundamental result.

6.4. Theorems. Let P be a pseudonorm on a vector space S, $S' = \mathscr{L}(P)$ and $P'(\varphi) = \|\varphi\|_P$ for $\varphi \in S'$. Then
(1) For every $\varphi \in S'$,

$$P'(\varphi) = \sup \{\, |\varphi(x)|; x \in S \text{ and } P(x) \leq 1\}.$$

(2) P' is a norm on S'.
(3) S' is complete in P'.

■ **proofs**
(1) Let $\varphi \in S'$ and $Q(\varphi) = \sup \{\, |\varphi(x)|; x \in S$ and $P(x) \leq 1\}$. Since $|\varphi(x)| \leq P'(\varphi) \cdot P(x)$ for $x \in S$, we have $Q(\varphi) \leq P'(\varphi)$. If $0 < r < P'(\varphi)$, then, for some $x \in S$, $|\varphi(x)| > r \cdot P(x)$; hence if $y = x/P(x)$,

then $P(y) = 1$ and $|\varphi(y)| > r$ so that $Q(\varphi) > r$. Thus, $Q(\varphi) \geq P'(\varphi)$ and therefore $Q(\varphi) = P'(\varphi)$.

(2) In view of (1), P' is clearly a pseudonorm. If $\varphi \neq \mathbf{0}$ so that $\varphi(x) \neq 0$ for some $x \in S$, then $0 < |\varphi(x)| \leq P'(\varphi) \cdot P(x)$ so that $P'(\varphi) > 0$. Thus, P' is a norm.

(3) Let φ be a Cauchy sequence in P'. For any $x \in S$, since

$$|\varphi_n(x) - \varphi_m(x)| = |(\varphi_n - \varphi_m)(x)| \leq P'(\varphi_n - \varphi_m) \cdot P(x),$$

we see that the $\varphi_n(x)$ form a Cauchy sequence of real numbers and hence there exists $\Psi(x) \in \mathscr{R}$ with $\Psi(x) = \lim_n \varphi_n(x)$. Clearly Ψ is a linear functional. If $M = \sup\{P'(\varphi_n); n \in \boldsymbol{\omega}\}$ then $M < \infty$, since $P'(\varphi_n) \leq P'(\varphi_m) + P'(\varphi_n - \varphi_m)$ and, for large m and n, $P'(\varphi_n - \varphi_m) < 1$. Thus, $|\Psi(x)| \leq M \cdot P(x)$ for every $x \in S$ and $\Psi \in S'$. To see that $\Psi = \lim_n \varphi_n$ in P', given $\epsilon > 0$ choose $N \in \boldsymbol{\omega}$ so that $P'(\varphi_n - \varphi_m) < \epsilon$ for $m, n > N$. Then, for such m, n and all $x \in S$, we have:

$$\begin{aligned} |(\Psi - \varphi_m)(x)| &\leq |\Psi(x) - \varphi_n(x)| + |(\varphi_n - \varphi_m)(x)| \\ &\leq |\Psi(x) - \varphi_n(x)| + \epsilon \cdot P(x). \end{aligned}$$

Taking the limit as $n \to \infty$ we get

$$|(\Psi - \varphi_m)(x)| \leq \epsilon \cdot P(x)$$

so that $P'(\Psi - \varphi_m) \leq \epsilon$. ■

A complete normed space is called a Banach space. Theorem 6.4 shows that the topological dual of any pseudonormed space is a Banach space. A main problem in the field of linear spaces is to characterize such duals. In the exercises we indicate characterizations for duals of ℓ_p spaces. In general the problem is closely connected with measure theory and integration. The most celebrated result in this connection is the Riesz representation theorem which characterizes the dual of $\mathbf{C}([0; 1])$ in terms of measures. It is discussed in Chapter 9.

6.5. Exercises

1. Let $n \in \boldsymbol{\omega}_+$, $S = \mathscr{R}_n$, $P(x) = \|x\|_2$ for $x \in S$. Show that $S^* = \mathscr{L}(P)$ and that for every $\varphi \in S^*$ there exists $a \in S$ such that $\varphi(x) = \langle x, a\rangle$ for every $x \in S$ and $\|\varphi\|_P = P(a)$.
2. Let $S = \ell_1$ and $P(x) = \|x\|_1$ for $x \in S$. Show that, for every $\varphi \in \mathscr{L}(P)$, there exists $a \in \ell_\infty$ such that $\varphi(x) = \langle x, a\rangle$ for $x \in S$ and $\|\varphi\|_P = \|a\|_\infty$.
3. Let $S = \{x \in \mathscr{R}^\omega : \lim_n x_n = 0\}$, so that $S \subset \ell_\infty$, and $P(x) = \|x\|_\infty$ for $x \in S$. Show that, for every $\varphi \in \mathscr{L}(P)$, there exists $a \in \ell_1$ such that $\varphi(x) = \langle x, a\rangle$ for every $x \in S$ and $\|\varphi\|_P = \|a\|_1$.
4. Let p, q be positive, $1/p + 1/q = 1$, $S = \ell_p$ and $P(x) = \|x\|_p$ for $x \in S$. Show that for every $\varphi \in \mathscr{L}(P)$ there exists $a \in \ell_q$ such that $\varphi(x) = \langle x, a\rangle$ for every $x \in S$ and $\|\varphi\|_P = \|a\|_q$.

PART II. MEASURE THEORY

The primary aim in Part II is to introduce some of the ideas of measure theory through the study of Lebesgue-Stieltjes measures on the line. The importance of these measures lies not only in their extensive use in so many branches of mathematics but also in the fact that they are the models on which the more general theories are based. Consider, for example, some of the aspects of Lebesgue measure on the line.

1. It is a nonnegative set function whose value on an interval is its length.
2. It is additive on a family of sets M which may be generated in a number of ways with or without reference to the topology.
3. The family M contains all the open and all the closed sets, and elements of M can be approximated in measure by open sets from above and by closed sets from below.
4. Through the integral, it gives rise to a linear functional on a space of functions containing the continuous functions vanishing outside a bounded interval.

Each of these aspects, singly or in combination, opens major avenues and points of view for the development of measure theory. Thus, in the classical theory of functions of a real variable, one looks at a measure as a generalization of the notions of length, volume, variation of a function, or, for physical applications, of mass, electric charge, and so forth. In probability theory, where "events" are interpreted as abstract sets, one looks at a measure as an additive set function on a family of abstract sets. In point set topology, aspect (3) leads to consideration of families of measures such as the Borel, Baire, Radón measures. In functional analysis, measure theory becomes a study of linear functionals on function spaces. Far from being in conflict, these various points of view actually complement each other and frequently, as in potential theory, they combine to produce significant results. Sooner or later therefore, the serious student must become familiar with more than one approach and be able to shift easily from one aspect of the theory to another.

In our development of the theory, we stress those notions and techniques whose applicability is not limited to the real line. Thus, many topics are discussed first in an abstract setting. The aim here, however, is not so much to give generalizations of classical results as to bring out the essential ideas involved and simplify the view. In the general situation, we study only results whose formulation would have been the same even if we had restricted our considerations to the real line.

We introduce the field through additive set functions, first in an abstract space and then in Euclidean space and the real line in particular. One of our main goals, however, is to establish fundamental bridges connecting set functions, functions of bounded variation, and linear functionals. We continue to use the underlying set-theoretic point of view established in the previous chapters not only for the sake of consistency, but because it constitutes the center through which passage from one aspect of measure theory to another is accomplished. It leads naturally and easily into any part of the theory and spotlights the interplay of measure-theoretic and topological concepts.

5. MEASURES ON ABSTRACT SPACES

1. INTRODUCTION

In this chapter we introduce some of the basic notions and techniques of measure theory which make no use of any underlying structure in the space. After defining additive functions and additive families of sets, we show that the study of additive functions can be reduced to that of the nonnegative ones. The highlight of this chapter is the description of a fundamental process due to Carathéodory for generating measures almost from scratch. This leads us naturally to the consideration of Carathéodory outer measures.

2. THE EXTENDED REAL LINE

Since we want to consider sets of infinite measure, we extend the real line $\mathscr{R}$ by adjoining two points, ∞ and $-\infty$. The order relation $<$ and the operations of addition and multiplication are also extended in a natural way, with the exception of $0 \cdot \infty$ and $\infty - \infty$. For measure-theoretic purposes, it is very convenient to let $0 \cdot \infty = 0$ (mainly because one is willing to neglect what happens on sets of measure zero), and we do so. On the other hand, $\infty - \infty$ remains undefined and by and large this reflects the fact that situations in which $\infty - \infty$ occur constitute major sources of difficulty in measure theory.

2.1. Definitions

(1) $\overline{\mathscr{R}} = \mathscr{R} \cup \{\infty, -\infty\}$,
$\overline{\mathscr{R}}_+ = \mathscr{R}_+ \cup \{\infty\}$.
For any $x \in \mathscr{R}$:

(2) $-\infty < x < \infty$ and $-\infty < \infty$.

(3) $x + \infty = \infty + x = \infty + \infty = \infty$,
$x - \infty = -\infty + x = -\infty - \infty = -\infty$.

(4) If $x > 0$, then $x \cdot \infty = \infty \cdot x = \infty \cdot \infty = (-\infty) \cdot (-\infty) = \infty$ and $x \cdot (-\infty) = (-\infty) \cdot x = \infty \cdot (-\infty) = (-\infty) \cdot \infty = -\infty$.
(5) If $x < 0$, then $x \cdot \infty = \infty \cdot x = -\infty$ and $x \cdot (-\infty) = (-\infty) \cdot x = \infty$.
(6) $0 \cdot \infty = \infty \cdot 0 = 0 \cdot (-\infty) = (-\infty) \cdot 0 = 0$.

Thus, the extended operations are still commutative and associative, but the distributive law does not hold in $\overline{\mathscr{R}}$, for example, $\infty \cdot (2 - 1) = \infty \cdot 1 = \infty$, but $(\infty \cdot 2) - (\infty \cdot 1) = \infty - \infty$ is undefined.

2.2. Definitions

(1) For $a, b \in \overline{\mathscr{R}}$:
$[a; b] = \{x \in \overline{\mathscr{R}}: a \leq x \leq b\}$.
$(a; b) = \{x \in \overline{\mathscr{R}}: a < x < b\}$.
$[a; b) = \{x \in \overline{\mathscr{R}}: a \leq x < b\}$.
$(a; b] = \{x \in \overline{\mathscr{R}}: a < x \leq b\}$.
An interval is any one of the above sets.
(2) U is a neighborhood of ∞ iff, for some $t \in \mathscr{R}$, $(t; \infty] \subset U$. U is a neighborhood of $-\infty$ iff, for some $t \in \mathscr{R}$, $[-\infty; t) \subset U$. For $x \in \mathscr{R}$, U is a neighborhood of x iff, for some $r > 0$, $(x - r; x + r) \subset U$.
(3) The usual topology for $\overline{\mathscr{R}}$ is the family of all $A \subset \overline{\mathscr{R}}$ such that for every $x \in A$ there exists a neighborhood U of x with $U \subset A$.

2.3. Exercise. The usual topology for $\overline{\mathscr{R}}$ is indeed a topology and $\overline{\mathscr{R}}$ is homeomorphic to $[-1; 1]$ so that $\overline{\mathscr{R}}$ is a compact space.

Other concepts are also easily extended from $\mathscr{R}$ to $\overline{\mathscr{R}}$. We mention in particular, unordered summation, which is of basic interest to our development of measure theory.

2.4. Definition

For any set A and function x on A to $\overline{\mathscr{R}}$, let $F' = \{\alpha: \alpha$ is finite, $\alpha \subset A$ and $x_n \geq 0$ for $n \in \alpha\}$, $F'' = \{\alpha: \alpha$ is finite, $\alpha \subset A$ and $x_n < 0$ for $n \in \alpha\}$. Then

$$\sum_{n \in A} x_n = \sup \{\sum_{n \in \alpha} x_n;\ \alpha \in F'\} + \inf \{\sum_{n \in \alpha} x_n;\ \alpha \in F''\}.$$

3. ADDITIVE FUNCTIONS AND FAMILIES

In this section we introduce the type of functions and families of sets with which measure theory is concerned and indicate a few of their elementary properties. We remind the reader that we are dealing with unordered summation in $\overline{\mathscr{R}}$ (see definition 2.4).

3.1. Definitions
Let H be any family of sets.

(1) μ is finitely additive on H iff μ is a function, $\phi \in H \subset$ domain μ, $\mu(\phi) = 0$, and, for every disjoint, finite family $F \subset H$ with $\bigcup F \in H$, we have

$$-\infty \leq \mu(\bigcup F) = \sum_{A \in F} \mu(A) \leq \infty.$$

(2) μ is σ-additive on H iff μ is a function, $\phi \in H \subset$ domain μ, $\mu(\phi) = 0$, and, for every disjoint, countable family $F \subset H$ with $\bigcup F \in H$, we have

$$-\infty \leq \mu(\bigcup F) = \sum_{A \in F} \mu(A) \leq \infty.$$

A σ-additive function is also frequently called a countably additive or completely additive function. We shall informally use the term additive function to refer to a function which is either finitely additive or σ-additive.

(3) μ is a measure on H iff μ is σ-additive on H and, for every $A \in H$, $\mu(A) \geq 0$.

3.2. Definitions
Let H be any family of sets.

(1) H is a ring iff $A \cup B \in H$ and $A \sim B \in H$ whenever $A, B \in H$.
(2) H is a σ-ring iff $\bigcup_{n \in \omega} A_n \in H$ and $A_0 \sim A_1 \in H$ whenever $A_n \in H$ for $n \in \boldsymbol{\omega}$.
(3) H is a field iff H is a ring and $\bigcup H \in H$.
(4) H is a σ-field iff H is a σ-ring and $\bigcup H \in H$.
(5) H is a σ-field in S iff $S = \bigcup H$ and H is a σ-field.

3.3. Definitions
Let H be any family of sets.

(1) $H_\sigma = \{B\colon B = \bigcup_{n \in \omega} A_n$ for some sequence A in $H\}$.
(2) $H_\delta = \{B\colon B = \bigcap_{n \in \omega} A_n$ for some sequence A in $H\}$.
(3) ring $H = \bigcap\{R\colon R$ is a ring and $H \subset R\}$.
(4) field $H = \bigcap\{F\colon F$ is a field and $H \subset F\}$.
(5) Borel ring $H = \bigcap\{R\colon R$ is a σ-ring and $H \subset R\}$.
(6) Borel field $H = \bigcap\{F\colon F$ is a σ-field and $H \subset F\}$.

We list next some elementary properties of the functions and families defined above.

3.4. Lemmas. Let H be a nonempty family of sets.
(1) If H is a ring, then $\phi \in H$ and $A \cap B \in H$ whenever $A, B \in H$.
(2) If H is a σ-ring, then $\phi \in H$ and $\bigcap_{n \in \omega} A_n \in H$ whenever $A_n \in H$ for $n \in \boldsymbol{\omega}$.

(3) If F is a family of rings or σ-rings or fields in a space S, or σ-fields in a space S, then $\bigcap F$ is also a ring or σ-ring or field in S, or σ-field in S, respectively.

(4) ring H, field H, Borel ring H, Borel field H are, respectively, the smallest ring, field, σ-ring, σ-field containing H.

■ **proofs:** These follow immediately from the definitions and elementary properties of sets. ■

3.5. Lemmas. Let H be a ring and μ be finitely additive on H.

(1) If $A, B \in H$, $A \subset B$, and $\mu(A) = \pm\infty$, then $\mu(A) = \mu(B)$.

(2) If $A, B \in H$, $A \subset B$, and $\mu(A) \neq \pm\infty$, then $\mu(B \sim A) = \mu(B) - \mu(A)$.

(3) There do not exist $A, B \in H$ with $\mu(A) = \infty$ and $\mu(B) = -\infty$.

■ **proofs:** Let $A, B \in H$.

(1), (2) If $A \subset B$, then $\mu(B) = \mu(A) + \mu(B \sim A)$; hence if $\mu(A) = \pm\infty$ we must have $\mu(B) = \mu(A)$ and if $\mu(A) \neq \pm\infty$ we can subtract and get $\mu(B) - \mu(A) = \mu(B \sim A)$.

(3) Suppose $\mu(A) = \infty$ and $\mu(B) = -\infty$. Then

$$\mu(A \cap B) + \mu(A \sim B) = \mu(A) = \infty,$$

$$\mu(B \cap A) + \mu(B \sim A) = \mu(B) = -\infty.$$

Thus, $\mu(A \cap B) \neq \pm\infty$ and hence $\mu(A \sim B) = \infty$ and $\mu(B \sim A) = -\infty$. Since $(A \sim B) \cap (B \sim A) = \phi$, we have

$$\mu((A \sim B) \cup (B \sim A)) = \mu(A \sim B) + \mu(B \sim A) = \infty - \infty,$$

which is impossible. ■

3.6. Theorems. Let H be a ring, μ be σ-additive on H and, for every $n \in \boldsymbol{\omega}$, $A_n \in H$.

(1) If $A_n \subset A_{n+1}$ for $n \in \boldsymbol{\omega}$ and $B = \bigcup_{n \in \boldsymbol{\omega}} A_n \in H$, then

$$\mu(B) = \lim_n \mu(A_n).$$

(2) If $A_n \supset A_{n+1}$ for $n \in \boldsymbol{\omega}$, $\mu(A_0) \neq \pm\infty$, and $B = \bigcap_{n \in \omega} A_n \in H$, then

$$\mu(B) = \lim_n \mu(A_n).$$

(3) If $B \in H$, $B \subset \bigcup_{n \in \boldsymbol{\omega}} A_n$, and μ is a measure on H, then

$$\mu(B) \leq \sum_{n \in \omega} \mu(A_n).$$

■ **proofs**

(1) If, for some $k \in \boldsymbol{\omega}$, $\mu(A_k) = \pm\infty$, then by 3.5.1, $\mu(B) = \mu(A_k) = \lim_n \mu(A_n)$. If, for every $k \in \boldsymbol{\omega}$, $\mu(A_k) \neq \pm\infty$, then, since

$$B = A_0 \cup \bigcup_{k \in \boldsymbol{\omega}} (A_{k+1} \sim A_k),$$

using the σ-additivity of μ and 3.5.2, we get

$$\mu(B) = \mu(A_0) + \sum_{k \in \omega} (\mu(A_{k+1}) - \mu(A_k)) = \lim_n \mu(A_n).$$

(2) By 3.5.1 we have $\mu(A_k) \neq \pm\infty$ for every $k \in \omega$. Since

$$A_0 = B \cup \bigcup_{k \in \omega} (A_k \sim A_{k+1}),$$

using the σ-additivity of μ and 3.5.2, we have

$$\begin{aligned}\mu(A_0) &= \mu(B) + \sum_{k \in \omega} (\mu(A_k) - \mu(A_{k+1})) \\ &= \mu(B) + \mu(A_0) - \lim_n \mu(A_n).\end{aligned}$$

Subtracting $\mu(A_0)$, we get

$$\mu(B) = \lim_n \mu(A_n).$$

(3) Let

$$C_n = B \cap A_n \sim \bigcup_{i=0}^{n-1} A_i.$$

Then $C_n \in H$, $C_n \subset A_n$ so that

$$\mu(A_n) = \mu(C_n) + \mu(A_n \sim C_n) \geq \mu(C_n)$$

and $C_m \cap C_n = \phi$ for $m, n \in \omega$ and $m \neq n$. Since $B = \bigcup_{n \in \omega} C_n$, we conclude

$$\mu(B) = \sum_{n \in \omega} \mu(C_n) \leq \sum_{n \in \omega} \mu(A_n). \blacksquare$$

3.7. Theorem. Let $A \in H$ and, for every $\alpha \in H$, let $\alpha \cap A \in H$ and $\nu(\alpha) = \mu(\alpha \cap A)$. If μ is finitely or σ-additive on H, then ν is finitely or σ-additive, respectively, on H.

■ **proof:** This follows immediately from the definitions and elementary properties of sets. ■

3.8. Exercises

1. Let H be a family of sets such that, for every $A, B \in H$, $A \cap B \in H$ there exists a disjoint, finite family $F \subset H$ with $A \sim B = \bigcup F$. Show that

$$\text{ring } H = \{\bigcup F;\ F \text{ is finite, disjoint and } F \subset H\}$$

and if μ is finitely additive on H, then there is a unique ν on ring H such that ν is finitely additive on ring H and $\nu(A) = \mu(A)$ for $A \in H$.

2. Let f be a function on $\mathscr{R}$ to $\mathscr{R}$, $H = \{[x; y);\ x, y \in \mathscr{R}\}$, and H' be the family of all bounded intervals. Then there exists a unique μ on ring H' such that μ is finitely additive on ring H' and $\mu([x; y]) = f(y) - f(x)$ whenever $-\infty < x \leq y < \infty$. If μ is σ-additive on ring H then,

for every $x \in \mathscr{R}, f(x) = \lim_{h \to 0^+} f(x - h)$, and if μ is σ-additive on ring H' then f is continuous.

3. Let $H = \{[x; y); x, y \in \mathscr{R}\}$. Then H_σ is not a σ-ring.
4. Let $H_0 = \{[x; y); x, y \in \mathscr{R}\}$, $\quad H_1 = \{[x; y]; x, y \in \mathscr{R}\}$,

$$H_2 = \{(x; y); x, y \in \mathscr{R}\}, \qquad H_3 = \{(x; y]; x, y \in \mathscr{R}\}.$$

Then Borel field H_i = Borel ring H_i = Borel ring H_j for $i, j = 0, 1, 2, 3$. Note that $(H_2)_\sigma$ is the family of all open sets in $\mathscr{R}$ and Borel field $H_2 \neq (H_2)_{\sigma\delta}$.

5. Let F be a family of functions on S to $\mathscr{R}$ such that if $f, g \in F$ then $f \pm g \in F$ and $f \cdot g \in F$. For any $A \subset S$, let 1_A be the characteristic function of A, that is,

$$1_A(x) = \begin{cases} 1 & \text{if} \quad x \in A \\ 0 & \text{if} \quad x \in S \sim A. \end{cases}$$

Let $H = \{A: A \subset S \text{ and } 1_A \in F\}$. Then H is a ring. If, for every monotone nondescending sequence f in F we have $\lim_n f_n \in F$, then H is a σ-ring. If l is a linear function on F to $\mathscr{R}$ and $\mu(A) = l(1_A)$ for $A \in H$, then μ is finitely additive on H.

6. Let H be a ring and $S = \bigcup H$. Then

$$\text{field } H = \{A: A \subset S \text{ and either } A \in H \text{ or } S \sim A \in H\}.$$

If H is a σ-ring, then field H = Borel field H. Show that there cannot be two disjoint sets in field $H \sim H$.

7. Let H be a ring, $S = \bigcup H$ and μ be finitely additive on H. If $S \notin H$, then, for any $t \in \mathscr{R}$, there is a unique ν on field H such that ν is finitely additive on field H, $\nu(S) = t$, and $\nu(A) = \mu(A)$ for $A \in H$. If H is a σ-ring and μ is σ-additive on H, then ν is σ-additive on field H = Borel field H.

8. Let S be an infinite space and $H = \{A: A \subset S \text{ and } A \text{ is finite}\}$. Then H is a ring. If

$$\nu(A) = \begin{cases} 0 & \text{if} \quad A \in H \\ 1 & \text{if} \quad S \sim A \in H, \end{cases}$$

then ν is finitely additive, but not σ-additive on field H.

9. Let S be an uncountable space and $H = \{A: A \subset S \text{ and } A \text{ is countable}\}$. Then H is a σ-ring. If

$$\nu(A) = \begin{cases} 0 & \text{if} \quad A \in H \\ 1 & \text{if} \quad A \notin H, \end{cases}$$

then ν is σ-additive on Borel field H, but is not even finitely additive on $\{A: A \subset S\}$.

4. VARIATION, JORDAN DECOMPOSITION

In this section we discuss a basic technique for constructing from a given additive function a nonnegative one. This enables us under some circumstances to represent an additive function as the difference of two nonnegative ones. The technique has its roots in the definition of variation of a function of a real variable (see exercise 4.3.1 and Chapter 9) and is also used, in a disguised form, to construct a nonnegative linear functional from an arbitrary one (see 4.3.3).

4.1. Definitions

For any set function μ to $\overline{\mathscr{R}}$ and $A \subset \bigcup$ domain μ:

(1) $\text{var}^+ \mu(A) = \sup \{\mu(\alpha);\ \alpha \in \text{domain } \mu \text{ and } \alpha \subset A\}$.
(2) $\text{var}^- \mu(A) = -\inf \{\mu(\alpha);\ \alpha \in \text{domain } \mu \text{ and } \alpha \subset A\}$.
(3) $\text{var}\, \mu(A) = \text{var}^+ \mu(A) + \text{var}^- \mu(A)$.

4.2. Theorem (Jordan decomposition). Let H be a ring and μ be finitely additive on H. If $\mu' = \text{var}^+ (\mu/H)$, $\mu'' = \text{var}^- (\mu/H)$, $S = \bigcup H$, and

$$F = \{A\colon A \subset S \text{ and either } A \in H \text{ or } S \sim A \in H\},$$

then:

(1) μ' and μ'' are nonnegative and finitely additive on F.
(2) If μ is σ-additive on H, then μ' and μ'' are σ-additive on F.
(3) If $A \in H$ and $\mu'(A) - \mu''(A) \in \overline{\mathscr{R}}$ then $\mu(A) = \mu'(A) - \mu''(A)$. (From 3.8.6, we know that F is a field and, if H is a σ-ring, then F is also a σ-field.)

■ **proofs**

(1) For any set A, since $\phi \subset A$ and $\mu(\phi) = 0$, we have $\mu'(A) \geq 0$ and $\mu''(A) \geq 0$. Let $A, B \in F$ and $A \cap B = \phi$. From 3.8.6 we must have $A \in H$ or $B \in H$. Suppose $A \in H$. If $\alpha \in H$ and $\alpha \subset A \cup B$, then $\alpha \cap A \in H$ and $\alpha \cap B = \alpha \sim A \in H$ so that

$$\mu(\alpha) = \mu(\alpha \cap A) + \mu(\alpha \sim A) \leq \mu'(A) + \mu'(B).$$

Thus, $\mu'(A \cup B) \leq \mu'(A) + \mu'(B)$. On the other hand, if $\alpha, \beta \in H$, $\alpha \subset A$ and $\beta \subset B$, then $\alpha \cup \beta \in H$ and

$$\mu(\alpha) + \mu(\beta) = \mu(\alpha \cup \beta) \leq \mu'(A \cup B).$$

Thus, $\mu'(A) + \mu'(B) = \mu'(A \cup B)$ and μ' is finitely additive on F. Since $\text{var}^- \mu = \text{var}^+ (-\mu)$, we see that μ'' is also finitely additive on F.

(2) Suppose μ is σ-additive on H, A is a sequence of disjoint elements of H, and $B = \bigcup_{n\in\omega} A_n$. If $\alpha \in H$ and $\alpha \subset B$, then $\alpha \cap A_n \in H$ for any $n \in \boldsymbol{\omega}$ and

$$\mu(\alpha) = \sum_{n\in\omega} \mu(\alpha \cap A_n) \leq \sum_{n\in\omega} \mu'(A_n).$$

Thus,

$$\mu'(B) \leq \sum_{n \in \omega} \mu'(A_n).$$

On the other hand, given $t < \Sigma_{n \in \omega} \mu'(A_n)$ we can find $N \in \boldsymbol{\omega}$ with $t < \Sigma_{n=0}^{N} \mu'(A_n)$ and then $\alpha_n \in H$ with $\alpha_n \subset A_n$ and $t < \Sigma_{n=0}^{N} \mu(\alpha_n)$. If $\beta = \bigcup_{n=0}^{N} \alpha_n$, then $\beta \in H$, $\beta \subset B$ and $\mu(\beta) > t$ so that $\mu'(B) > t$. Thus,

$$\mu'(B) \geq \sum_{n \in \omega} \mu'(A_n)$$

and μ' is σ-additive on H. Since, by 3.8.6, there cannot be two disjoint elements in $F \sim H$, we conclude with the help of (1) that μ' is σ-additive on F. Similarly for μ''.

(3) Let $A \in H$ and $\mu'(A) - \mu''(A) \in \overline{\mathscr{R}}$ so that we cannot have $\mu'(A) = \mu''(A) = \infty$. Suppose $\mu''(A) < \infty$. Then we have only to check that $\mu'(A) = \mu(A) + \mu''(A)$. If $\mu(A) = \infty$, then $\mu'(A) = \infty$ and $\mu'(A) = \mu(A) + \mu''(A)$. If $\mu(A) \neq \infty$, then for any $\alpha \in H$ with $\alpha \subset A$ we have $\mu(\alpha) \neq \pm\infty$ and

$$\begin{aligned}\mu(A) + \mu''(A) &= \mu(A) + \sup\{-\mu(\alpha); \alpha \in H, \alpha \subset A\} \\ &= \sup\{\mu(A) - \mu(\alpha); \alpha \in H, \alpha \subset A\} \\ &= \sup\{\mu(A \sim \alpha); \alpha \in H, \alpha \subset A\} \\ &= \sup\{\mu(\alpha); \alpha \in H, \alpha \subset A\} \\ &= \mu'(A). \blacksquare\end{aligned}$$

Remark. In case H is a σ-ring and μ is σ-additive on H, there is a deeper result, known as the Hahn decomposition, which gives more information than 4.2. It produces a $P \in H$ such that $\text{var}^+ \mu$ agrees with μ on the subsets of P which belong to H and $\text{var}^- \mu$ agrees with $-\mu$ on the subsets of $S \sim P$ which belong to H. Thus, there is a portion of the space S on which μ is positive and on the complement of which μ is negative. Although the proof of this theorem is within our reach now, we delay its introduction until Chapter 8 because its main applications are concerned with differentiation.

4.3. Exercises

1. Let f be on $\mathscr{R}$ to $\mathscr{R}$, $H = \{[x; y); x, y \in \mathscr{R}\}$ and, referring to 3.8.2, let μ be the finitely additive function on ring H such that $\mu([x; y)) = f(y) - f(x)$ for $-\infty < x \leq y < \infty$. For any $a < b$, the total variation of f over (a, b) is

$$V(a; b) = \sup\left\{\sum_{i=0}^{n} |f(x_{i+1}) - f(x_i)|;\ n \in \boldsymbol{\omega} \text{ and } a < x_i < x_{i+1} < b \text{ for } i = 0, \cdots, n\right\}.$$

Check that $V(a; b) = \text{var}\,\mu((a; b))$ and that if $V(a; b) < \infty$, then there exist nondecreasing functions f' and f'' such that, for every $x \in (a; b), f(x) = f'(x) - f''(x)$.

2. Referring to (1), determine whether the total variation of f over $(0; 1)$ is finite when

$$\text{(a) } f(x) = \sin(1/x), \quad \text{(b) } f(x) = x \sin(1/x), \quad \text{(c) } f(x) = x^2 \sin(1/x).$$

3. Let

$$C = \{f : f \text{ is continuous on } \mathscr{R} \text{ to } \mathscr{R} \text{ and there exists } K \in \mathscr{R}_+ \text{ such that } f(x) = 0 \text{ for } x \in \mathscr{R} \text{ with } |x| > K\}$$

$$C_+ = \{f \in C : f(x) \geq 0 \text{ for } x \in \mathscr{R}\},$$

and l be a linear functional on C.

(a) If $l(f) \geq 0$ for every $f \in C_+$, then, for every $K \in \mathscr{R}_+$ there exists $M_K \in \mathscr{R}_+$ such that $|l(f)| \leq M_K \cdot \|f\|_\infty$ for every $f \in C$ with $f(x) = 0$ for $|x| > K$.

(b) If, for every $K \in \mathscr{R}_+$ there exists $M_K \in \mathscr{R}_+$ such that $|l(f)| \leq M_K \|f\|_\infty$ for every $f \in C$ with $f(x) = 0$ for $|x| > K$, then there exist linear functionals l' and l'' such that $l'(f) \geq 0$ and $l''(f) \geq 0$ for every $f \in C_+$ and $l(f) = l'(f) - l''(f)$ for every $f \in C$.
(*Hint:* for $f \in C_+$, let $l'(f) - \sup \{l(g);\ g \subset C_+ \text{ and } g \leq f\}$.)

5. CARATHÉODORY MEASURES

In view of the Jordan decomposition theorem, in developing the theory of σ-additive functions we may restrict ourselves to measures. Now, it is very seldom that the domain of a measure consists of all the subsets of a space S. It is just as seldom that one picks a σ-field *a priori* and then defines directly a measure on it. Almost always one starts with some family H of subsets of S (for example, intervals) and a nonnegative function τ on H (for example, length of intervals) and then one tries to generate a measure from these. In this section we discuss a fundamental process for doing so which is due to C. Carathéodory. It consists of two parts. First, it produces from τ and H a function μ defined on *all* the subsets of S. This μ, however, is not σ-additive in general, but only subadditive. The second part of the process then picks a σ-field M on which μ is σ-additive. Such nonnegative, subadditive functions μ are called Carathéodory measures and the elements of the σ-field M are called μ-measurable sets. With any luck (see theorem 5.4.4), it may turn out that $H \subset M$ and hence Borel field $H \subset M$. It is very common to consider only such situations and then to restrict μ to Borel field H so that a theorem is formulated which yields only an extension of τ from H to Borel field H. Such a restriction, however, is quite arbitrary and unnatural. It frequently complicates a problem unnecessarily instead of simplifying it and blocks consideration of some important questions such as whether certain sets are measurable or not. When more than one measure is involved, the natural family to consider is that consisting of those sets which are μ-measurable for all μ under discussion. Such sets are called absolutely or universally measurable.

5.1. Definitions

(1) μ is a Carathéodory measure on S iff μ is a function on the family of all subsets of S such that $\mu(\phi) = 0$ and

$$0 \leq \mu(A) \leq \sum_{n \in \omega} \mu(B_n) \leq \infty$$

whenever $A \subset \bigcup_{n \in \omega} B_n \subset S$.

(2) For μ a Carathéodory measure on S:
A is μ-measurable iff $A \subset S$ and, for every $T \subset S$

$$\mu(T) = \mu(T \cap A) + \mu(T \sim A).$$

(3) $\mathscr{M}_\mu = \{A: A \text{ is } \mu\text{-measurable}\}$.

(4) μ is an H-outer measure on S iff μ is a Carathéodory measure on S, $H \subset \mathscr{M}_\mu$ and, for every $A \subset S$,

$$\mu(A) = \inf \{\mu(\alpha);\ \alpha \in H \quad \text{and} \quad A \subset \alpha\}.$$

(5) μ is an outer measure on S iff μ is an $\mathscr{M}_\mu$-outer measure on S.

(6) μ is the Carathéodory measure on S generated by τ and H iff
  (i) H is a family of subsets of S with $\phi \in H$,
  (ii) $\tau(\phi) = 0$ and $\tau(\alpha) \geq 0$ for $\alpha \in H$,
  (iii) for any $A \subset S$,

$$\mu(A) = \inf \left\{ \sum_{\alpha \in H'} \tau(\alpha);\ H' \text{ is countable, } H' \subset H, A \subset \bigcup H' \right\}.$$

(Recall that $\inf \phi = \infty$ so that if A cannot be covered by a countable subfamily of H, then $\mu(A) = \infty$.)

Remark on terminology. In his original paper,* C. Carathéodory was primarily interested in studying length and surface area in Euclidean space, so the set functions he considered had many more conditions imposed on them than are found in the above definitions. What we call a Carathéodory measure is frequently referred to in the literature as a Carathéodory outer measure or simply an outer measure. What we call an outer measure is sometimes called a regular outer measure. Unfortunately, the term "regular outer measure" is also frequently used to denote a measure in a topological space satisfying various approximation properties (say by open sets from above and by closed or compact sets from below). The overuse of the term regular in the mathematical

* C. Carathéodory, *Nachrichten Gesellschaft der Wissenschaften zu Göttingén* 1914, pp. 405.

literature is responsible for our avoiding it altogether in this context. Since all extensions of measures by the Carathéodory process (5.1.6) are outer measures in our sense (theorem 5.4) as are in fact just about all Carathéodory measures one meets in practice, the distinction between Carathéodory measure and outer measure is not very important, so our terminology is not in serious conflict with that found in the literature.

We collect together next the fundamental theorems about Carathéodory measures. The proofs are given after all the statements of the theorems.

5.2. Theorems. Let μ be a Carathéodory measure on S.

(1) If $\mu(A) = 0$, then $A \in \mathscr{M}_\mu$.

(2) μ is σ-additive on $\mathscr{M}_\mu$.

(3) $\mathscr{M}_\mu$ is a σ-field in S.

5.3. Theorems. Let μ be an outer measure on S. Then:

(1) for every $A \subset S$, there exists $B \in \mathscr{M}_\mu$ with $A \subset B$ and $\mu(A) = \mu(B)$

(2) If, for every $n \in \boldsymbol{\omega}$, $A_n \subset A_{n+1} \subset S$, then $\mu(\bigcup_{n\in\omega} A_n) = \lim_n \mu(A_n)$.

(3) If $A \subset S$ and $\mu(S) = \mu(A) + \mu(S \sim A) < \infty$, then $A \in \mathscr{M}_\mu$.

5.4. Theorems. Let μ be the Carathéodory measure on S generated by τ and H. Then:

(1) μ is a Carathéodory measure on S.

(2) For any $A \subset S$,

$$\mu(A) = \inf\{\mu(\alpha); \alpha \in H_\sigma \quad \text{and} \quad A \subset \alpha\}.$$

(3) If A can be covered by a countable subfamily of H (in particular, if $\mu(A) < \infty$), then there exists $B \in H_{\sigma\delta}$ with $A \subset B$ and $\mu(A) = \mu(B)$.

(4) If H is a ring and τ is finitely additive on H, then $H \subset \mathscr{M}_\mu$ and μ is an H_σ-outer measure.

(5) If H is a ring and τ is σ-additive on H, then $\tau(\alpha) = \mu(\alpha)$ for $\alpha \in H$ (so that $\mu/\mathscr{M}_\mu$ is a measure which extends τ from H to a σ-field containing H).

■ **proof of 5.2:** We give the proof in a series of lemmas.

5.2.(a) Lemma. $A \in \mathscr{M}_\mu$ iff, for every T with $\mu(T) < \infty$,

$$\mu(T) \geq \mu(T \cap A) + \mu(T \sim A).$$

■ **proof:** We always have $\mu(T) \leq \mu(T \cap A) + \mu(T \sim A)$.

5.2.(b) Lemma. $A \in \mathscr{M}_\mu$ iff $S \sim A \in \mathscr{M}_\mu$.

5.2.(c) Lemma. If $\mu(A) = 0$, then $A \in \mathscr{M}_\mu$. Thus, $\phi, S \in \mathscr{M}_\mu$.

■ **proof:** If $\mu(A) = 0$, then $\mu(T \cap A) = 0$ and $\mu(T \sim A) \leq \mu(T)$ for any $T \subset S$.

5.2.(d) Lemma. If A is a sequence of disjoint sets in $\mathscr{M}_\mu$ and $B = \bigcup_{n\in\omega} A_n$, then $B \in \mathscr{M}_\mu$ and

$$\mu(B) = \sum_{n\in\omega} \mu(A_n).$$

■ **proof:** Let $T \subset S$. Since $A_n \in \mathscr{M}_\mu$, we have:

$$\mu(T) = \mu(T \cap A_0) + (T \sim A_0).$$
$$\mu(T \sim A_0) = \mu((T \sim A_0) \cap A_1) + \mu((T \sim A_0) \sim A_1)$$
$$= \mu(T \cap A_1) + \mu(T \sim (A_0 \cup A_1)).$$

Thus,

$$\mu(T) = \mu(T \cap A_0) + \mu(T \cap A_1) + \mu(T \sim (A_0 \cup A_1)).$$

By induction, for any $N \in \boldsymbol{\omega}$:

$$\mu(T) = \sum_{n=0}^{N} \mu(T \cap A_n) + \mu\left(T \sim \bigcup_{n=0}^{N} A_n\right)$$
$$\geq \sum_{n=0}^{N} \mu(T \cap A_n) + \mu(T \sim B).$$

Letting $N \to \infty$, we get

$$\mu(T) \geq \sum_{n\in\omega} \mu(T \cap A_n) + \mu(T \sim B)$$
$$\geq \mu(T \cap B) + \mu(T \sim B).$$

Thus, $B \in \mathscr{M}_\mu$ and, letting $T = B$ above, we get

$$\mu(B) \geq \sum_{n\in\omega} \mu(A_n) \geq \mu(B).$$

5.2.(e) Lemma. If $A, B \in \mathscr{M}_\mu$, then $A \sim B \in \mathscr{M}_\mu$.

■ **proof:** Let $T \subset S$. Then

$$\mu(T) = \mu(T \cap A) + \mu(T \sim A)$$
$$= \mu((T \cap A) \sim B) + \mu((T \cap A) \cap B) + \mu(T \sim A)$$
$$\geq \mu(T \cap (A \sim B)) + \mu(T \sim (A \sim B)),$$

since $T \sim (A \sim B) = (T \cap A \cap B) \cup (T \sim A)$.

5.2.(f) Lemma. If $A_n \in \mathscr{M}_\mu$ for $n \in \boldsymbol{\omega}$, then $\bigcup_{n\in\omega} A_n \in \mathscr{M}_\mu$.

■ **proof:** Let

$$B_n = A_n \sim \bigcup_{i=0}^{n-1} A_i.$$

Then $B_m \cap B_n = \phi$ for $m, n \in \boldsymbol{\omega}$ and $m \neq n$ and

$$\bigcup_{i=0}^{n} A_i = \bigcup_{i=0}^{n} B_i.$$

Hence by lemmas 5.2d, e and induction we see that $B_n \in \mathscr{M}_\mu$ and hence by 5.2d:

$$\bigcup_{n\in\omega} A_n = \bigcup_{n\in\omega} B_n \in \mathscr{M}_\mu. \ ■$$

■ **proof of 5.3:** Let μ be an outer measure on S.

(1) Let $A \subset S$. If $\mu(A) = \infty$, then $A \subset S \in \mathscr{M}_\mu$ and $\mu(A) = \mu(S)$. If $\mu(A) < \infty$, then for every $n \in \omega$ there exists $\alpha_n \in \mathscr{M}_\mu$ with $A \subset \alpha_n$ and $\mu(\alpha_n) < \mu(A) + 1/(n + 1)$. Let $B = \bigcap_{n\in\omega} \alpha_n$. Then $A \subset B \in \mathscr{M}_\mu$ and $\mu(B) \le \lim_n \mu(\alpha_n) \le \mu(A) \le \mu(B)$.

(2) Let $A_n \subset A_{n+1} \subset S$ for $n \in \omega$ and $A' = \bigcup_{n\in\omega} A_n$. By (1), there exist $B_n \in \mathscr{M}_\mu$ with $A_n \subset B_n$ and $\mu(A_n) = \mu(B_n)$. Let $C_n = \bigcup_{i=0}^n B_i$. If $\mu(A_k) = \infty$ for some $k \in \omega$, then $\mu(A') = \infty = \lim_n \mu(A_n)$. If $\mu(A_n) < \infty$ for every $n \in \omega$, then, for $i = 0, \cdots, n$, since $A_i \subset B_n \cap B_i$, we have

$$\mu(A_i) \le \mu(B_n \cap B_i) \le \mu(B_i) = \mu(A_i)$$

and hence

$$\mu(B_i \sim B_n) = \mu(B_i) - \mu(B_n \cap B_i) = 0.$$

Thus, $A_n \subset C_n \subset C_{n+1}$ and

$$\mu(A_n) \le \mu(C_n) \le \mu(B_n) + \sum_{i=0}^{n} \mu(B_i \sim B_n) = \mu(B_n) = \mu(A_n).$$

Since $C_n \in \mathscr{M}_\mu$ and μ is σ-additive on $\mathscr{M}_\mu$, by 3.6.1, we have

$$\lim_n \mu(A_n) = \lim_n \mu(C_n) = \mu\left(\bigcup_{n\in\omega} C_n\right) \ge \mu(A') \ge \lim_n \mu(A_n).$$

(3) Suppose $A \subset S$ and $\mu(S) = \mu(A) + \mu(S \sim A) < \infty$. By (1), let $B \in \mathscr{M}_\mu$, $S \sim A \subset B$, $\mu(S \sim A) = \mu(B)$ and $B' = S \sim B$. Then $B' \subset A$ and

$$\mu(B) + \mu(B') = \mu(S) = \mu(A) + \mu(S \sim A).$$

Hence $\mu(B') = \mu(A)$ and, since $B' \in \mathscr{M}_\mu$,

$$\mu(B') = \mu(A) = \mu(B') + \mu(A \sim B').$$

Thus, $\mu(A \sim B') = 0$, $A \sim B' \in \mathscr{M}_\mu$ and $A = B' \cup (A \sim B') \in \mathscr{M}_\mu$. ■

■ **proof of 5.4:** Let μ be the Carathéodory measure on S generated by τ and H.

(1) Clearly, μ is nonnegative and $\mu(\phi) = 0$. Let $A \subset \bigcup_{n\in\omega} B_n \subset S$. If, for some $n \in \omega$, $\mu(B_n) = \infty$, then

$$\mu(A) \le \sum_{n\in\omega} \mu(B_n).$$

Suppose, for every $n \in \omega$, $\mu(B_n) < \infty$. Given $\epsilon > 0$, let F_n be a countable subfamily of H covering B_n and such that

$$\sum_{\alpha\in F_n} \tau(\alpha) < \mu(B_n) + \epsilon/2^{n+1}$$

and let $H' = \bigcup_{n\in\omega} F_n$. Then H' is a countable subfamily of H covering A and

$$\mu(A) \leq \sum_{\alpha\in H'} \tau(\alpha) \leq \sum_{n\in\omega} \sum_{\alpha\in F_n} \tau(\alpha) \leq \sum_{n\in\omega} \mu(B_n) + \epsilon.$$

Thus, μ is a Carathéodory measure on S.

(2) Let $A \subset S$. If A cannot be covered by a countable subfamily of H then $\mu(A) = \infty$ and

$$\inf\{\mu(\alpha); \alpha \in H_\sigma \quad \text{and} \quad A \subset \alpha\} = \inf \phi = \infty = \mu(A).$$

Otherwise, given $\epsilon > 0$, there exists a countable subfamily H' of H covering A and such that

$$\sum_{\alpha\in H'} \tau(\alpha) \leq \mu(A) + \epsilon.$$

Let $\beta = \bigcup H'$. Then $A \subset \beta \in H_\sigma$ and

$$\mu(\beta) \leq \sum_{\alpha\in H'} \tau(\alpha) \leq \mu(A) + \epsilon.$$

(3) Suppose A can be covered by a countable subfamily of H. By (2), for every $n \in \boldsymbol{\omega}$, there exists $\alpha_n \in H_\sigma$ with $A \subset \alpha_n$ and $\mu(\alpha_n) \leq \mu(A) + 1/(n+1)$. Let $B = \bigcap_{n\in\omega} \alpha_n$. Then $A \subset B \in H_{\sigma\delta}$ and

$$\mu(A) \leq \mu(B) \leq \lim_n \mu(\alpha_n) \leq \mu(A).$$

(4) Suppose H is a ring and τ is finitely additive on H. Let $A \in H$. Given $T \subset S$ with $\mu(T) < \infty$ and $\epsilon > 0$, let H' be a countable subfamily of H covering T and such that

$$\sum_{\alpha\in H'} \tau(\alpha) < \mu(T) + \epsilon.$$

Then

$$\mu(T \cap A) + \mu(T \sim A) \leq \sum_{\alpha\in H'} \tau(\alpha \cap A) + \sum_{\alpha\in H'} \tau(\alpha \sim A)$$

$$= \sum_{\alpha\in H'} \tau(\alpha) < \mu(T) + \epsilon.$$

Hence, by lemma 5.2a, $A \in \mathcal{M}_\mu$. Thus, $H \subset \mathcal{M}_\mu$ and therefore $H_\sigma \subset \mathcal{M}_\mu$ so that, by (2), μ is an H_σ-outer measure.

(5) Suppose H is a ring and τ is σ-additive on H. Let $A \in H$. Clearly $\mu(A) \leq \tau(A)$. On the other hand, if $\alpha_n \in H$ for $n \in \boldsymbol{\omega}$ and $A \subset \bigcup_{n\in\omega} \alpha_n$, then, by 3.6.3, $\tau(A) \leq \Sigma_{n\in\omega} \tau(\alpha_n)$. Thus, $\tau(A) \leq \mu(A)$. ∎

5.5. Exercises

1. Trivial measures: Let $0 \leq t \leq \infty$, $\mu(\phi) = 0$, and $\mu(A) = t$ whenever $\phi \neq A \subset S$. Check that μ is a Carathéodory measure on S and determine $\mathcal{M}_\mu$.

2. Point mass: Let $x \in S$ and

$$\mu(A) = \begin{cases} 1 & \text{if} \quad x \in A \subset S \\ 0 & \text{if} \quad x \notin A \subset S. \end{cases}$$

Check that μ is a Carathéodory measure on S and determine $\mathscr{M}_\mu$.

3. Counting measure: For any $A \subset S$, let $\mu(A)$ be the number of points in A if A is finite and $\mu(A) = \infty$ if A is infinite. Check that μ is a Carathéodory measure on S and determine $\mathscr{M}_\mu$. If $\tau(\{x\}) = 1$ for $x \in S$ and $H = \{\{x\}; x \in S\}$, then μ is the Carathéodory measure generated by τ and H.

4. Let S be an uncountable space and, for any $A \subset S$,

$$\mu(A) = \begin{cases} 0 & \text{if} \quad A \text{ is countable} \\ 1 & \text{if} \quad A \text{ is uncountable.} \end{cases}$$

Check that μ is a Carathéodory measure on S and determine $\mathscr{M}_\mu$.

5. Let μ be a Carathéodory measure on S and $A \subset S$. Check that:
   (i) if $B \in \mathscr{M}_\mu$, $B \subset A$, and $\mu(B) < \infty$, then

$$\mu(A \sim B) = \mu(A) - \mu(B).$$

   (ii) if $\mu(A) = \sup \{\mu(B); B \in \mathscr{M}_\mu \text{ and } B \subset A\} < \infty$, then $A \in \mathscr{M}_\mu$.

6. Restriction of a measure: Let μ be a Carathéodory measure on S and $T \subset S$. The restriction of μ to T is the function μ_T such that, for every $A \subset S$, $\mu_T(A) = \mu(T \cap A)$. Check that:
   (a) $\mathscr{M}_\mu \subset \mathscr{M}_{\mu_T}$.
   (b) If $T \in \mathscr{M}_\mu$ and $A \subset T$, then $A \in \mathscr{M}_\mu$ iff $A \in \mathscr{M}_{\mu_T}$.
   (c) $\mathscr{M}_\mu = \bigcap \{\mathscr{M}_{\mu_T}; T \subset S \text{ and } \mu(T) < \infty\}$.

7. Sum, Sup, Inf of measures: Let M be a nonempty family of Carathéodory measures on S and, for every $A \subset S$,

$$\nu(A) = \sum_{\mu \in M} \mu(A),$$
$$\nu'(A) = \sup \{\mu(A); \mu \in M\},$$
$$\nu''(A) = \inf \{\mu(A); \mu \in M\}.$$

   Check that:
   (a) ν is a Carathéodory measure on S and $\bigcap_{\mu \in M} \mathscr{M}_\mu \subset \mathscr{M}_\nu$.
   (b) ν' is a Carathéodory measure on S, but we need not have $\bigcap_{\mu \in M} \mathscr{M}_\mu \subset \mathscr{M}_{\nu'}$.
   (c) ν'' need not be a Carathéodory measure on S.

8. Image of a measure: Let μ be a Carathéodory measure on S and f be a function on S to S'. For any $A' \subset S'$, let $\nu(A') = \mu(f^{-1}[A'])$. Then ν is a Carathéodory measure on S' and if $A' \subset S'$ and $f^{-1}[A'] \in \mathscr{M}_\mu$, then $A' \in \mathscr{M}_\nu$.

9. Outer, inner measure: Let μ be a Carathéodory measure on S and, for any $A \subset S$,

$$\bar{\mu}(A) = \inf\{\mu(\alpha);\ \alpha \in \mathscr{M}_\mu \quad \text{and} \quad A \subset \alpha\},$$
$$\underline{\mu}(A) = \sup\{\mu(\alpha);\ \alpha \in \mathscr{M}_\mu \quad \text{and} \quad \alpha \subset A\}.$$

Check that:
(a) $\bar{\mu}$ is a Carathéodory measure on S, but $\underline{\mu}$ need not be one.
(b) $\mathscr{M}_\mu \subset \mathscr{M}_{\bar{\mu}}$.
(c) If $A \in \mathscr{M}_{\bar{\mu}}$ and $\bar{\mu}(A) < \infty$, then $A \in \mathscr{M}_\mu$.
(d) If $\mu(A) < \infty$, then

$$A \in \mathscr{M}_\mu \text{ iff } \mu(A) = \underline{\mu}(A) \text{ iff } \bar{\mu}(A) = \underline{\mu}(A).$$

(e) $\bar{\bar{\mu}} = \bar{\mu}$.
(f) If $A \cap B \neq \phi$ and $A \cup B \in \mathscr{M}_\mu$, then $\mu(A \cup B) = \bar{\mu}(A) + \underline{\mu}(B)$.
Note that μ is an outer measure on S iff $\mu = \bar{\mu}$. Thus, $\bar{\mu}$ and $\underline{\mu}$ are called respectively the outer and inner measure generated by μ.

6. LEBESGUE-STIELTJES MEASURES

1. INTRODUCTION

In this chapter we discuss a classical family of measures which extend the notions of length, area, volume, mass, and so forth, to a wider class of sets than the class of elementary geometric figures. We study them first on the real line emphasizing their connection with monotone functions and then consider n-dimensional Euclidean space where we concentrate on the most important one, n-dimensional Lebesgue measure. These measures are used extensively in analysis and probability, to a large extent because they are closely connected with the topology of the space on which they are defined. They exhibit many of the important characteristics of more general measures, in particular, topological measures. Thus, a good grasp of their behavior is an excellent stepping-stone for proceeding more deeply into the field.

Their definition and elementary properties illustrate the ideas discussed in Chapter 5. We try to suggest how one might proceed in more general topological situations by adopting formulations of theorems and methods of proof which make as little use as possible of too special properties of Euclidean space.

2. LEBESGUE-STIELTJES MEASURES ON THE LINE

The definition of a Lebesgue-Stieltjes measure given below establishes a fundamental method for passing from a monotone function of a real variable to a measure. As a result, one can study properties of the function through the measure. For example, integration and differentiation with respect to and of the function will be discussed in later chapters within the context of integration and differentiation with respect to and of the measure.

The reader might get a better appreciation of concepts and terminology in measure theory if he were to bear in mind that, through this fundamental connection between measures and functions on the line, a great many of the measure-theoretic techniques have their roots in methods originally used in the theory of functions of a real variable.

As a simple motivation for the concepts and work below, consider the following. Let finite mass be distributed on the real line so that, for any $x \in \mathscr{R}$, $f(x)$ represents the mass of the interval $(-\infty; x)$. Then f is nondecreasing and, for $-\infty < x < y < \infty$, $f(y) - f(x)$ represents the mass of $[x; y)$. Let $\tau([x; y)) = f(y) - f(x)$. Assuming that mass is σ-additive on intervals, that is that f is continuous on the left (Chapter 5, exercise 3.8.2), one is led to consider a measure on a σ-field which extends τ. This is what the Lebesgue-Stieltjes measure generated by f does. If we wanted to compute the moment of mass about the origin, then, following the standard argument used in elementary calculus, we would consider limits of sums of the form

$$\sum_i a_i(f(x_{i+1}) - f(x_i)),$$

where $x_i \le a_i < x_{i+1}$. This leads to $\int x\, df(x)$ and more generally to integration with respect to f or the Lebesgue-Stieltjes measure generated by f.

We concentrate here on monotone, nondecreasing functions, but in view of the Jordan decomposition and exercise 4.3.1 of Chapter 5, the ideas apply also to functions of bounded variation. We shall return to this point in Chapter 9 after we have developed more measure-theoretic tools.

2.1. Definitions

(1) f is nondecreasing on $\mathscr{R}$ iff f is on $\mathscr{R}$ to $\mathscr{R}$ and, for every $x, y \in \mathscr{R}$ with $x \le y$, we have $f(x) \le f(y)$.

(2) For f a nondecreasing function on $\mathscr{R}$:

The Lebesgue-Stieltjes outer measure generated by f is the function μ defined, for every $A \subset \mathscr{R}$, by

$$\mu(A) = \inf\left\{\sum_{i\in\omega}(f(y_i) - f(x_i));\ -\infty < x_i \le y_i < \infty \text{ for } i \in \omega \text{ and } A \subset \bigcup_{i\in\omega}(x_i; y_i)\right\}.$$

The Lebesgue-Stieltjes measure generated by f is $\mu/\mathscr{M}_\mu$.

Note that μ is the Carathéodory measure on $\mathscr{R}$ generated by τ and H, where $H = \{(x; y); x, y \in \mathscr{R}\}$ and $\tau((x; y)) = f(y) - f(x)$ for $x \le y$. The fact that f is nondecreasing guarantees that τ is nonnegative and hence that μ is a Carathéodory measure. The fact H is a base for the topology on $\mathscr{R}$ is responsible for the connection between μ and the topology.

We now list the fundamental properties of Lebesgue-Stieltjes measures.

2.2. Theorem. Let f be nondecreasing on $\mathscr{R}$; μ be the Lebesgue-Stieltjes outer measure generated by f; for $x \in \mathscr{R}$,

$$\bar{f}(x) = \lim_{h \to 0^+} f(x + h), \qquad \underline{f}(x) = \lim_{h \to 0^+} f(x - h);$$

and $-\infty < a \leq b < \infty$. Then:

(1) $\mu(\{a\}) = \bar{f}(a) - \underline{f}(a)$ so that $\mu(\{a\}) = 0$ iff f is continuous at a.

(2) $\{x: \mu(\{x\}) > 0\}$ is countable.

(3) Open sets are μ-measurable.

(4)
$$\mu([a; b]) = \bar{f}(b) - \underline{f}(a), \qquad \mu((a; b)) = \underline{f}(b) - \bar{f}(a),$$
$$\mu([a; b)) = \underline{f}(b) - \underline{f}(a), \qquad \mu((a; b]) = \bar{f}(b) - \bar{f}(a).$$

Thus, if f is continuous on the left, then $\mu([a; b)) = f(b) - f(a)$, and if f is continuous on the right, then $\mu((a; b]) = f(b) - f(a)$.

(5) For every $A \subset \mathscr{R}$,

$$\mu(A) = \inf \{\mu(\alpha); \alpha \text{ is open and } A \subset \alpha\},$$

that is, μ is a $\mathscr{G}$-outer measure, where $\mathscr{G}$ is the family of open sets.

(6) For every $A \in \mathscr{M}_\mu$,

$$\mu(A) = \sup \{\mu(C); C \text{ is compact and } C \subset A\}.$$

(7) $\mu =$ The Lebesgue-Stieltjes outer measure generated by $\bar{f}$;
$\mu =$ The Lebesgue-Stieltjes outer measure generated by $\underline{f}$.

■ **proofs**

(1) This is immediate from the definition.

(2) We first check that, for any $\epsilon > 0$, $\{x \in (a; b): \mu(\{x\}) > \epsilon\}$ is finite. Indeed let $N \in \boldsymbol{\omega}$, $a < x_0 < x_1 < \cdots < x_N < b$ and $\mu(\{x_i\}) > \epsilon$ for $i = 0, \cdots, N$. Choose α_i, β_i so that $a < \alpha_i < x_i < \beta_i < \alpha_{i+1} < b$. Then

$$f(b) - f(a) \geq \sum_{i=0}^{N} (f(\beta_i) - f(\alpha_i)) \geq \sum_{i=0}^{N} \mu(\{x_i\}) > (N + 1) \cdot \epsilon.$$

Thus, there cannot be more than $(f(b) - f(a))/\epsilon$ points x with $\mu(\{x\}) > \epsilon$ in $(a; b)$. Since

$$\{x: \mu(\{x\}) > 0\} = \bigcup_{n \in \omega} \bigcup_{K \in \omega} \{x \in (-K; K): \mu(\{x\}) > 1/(n + 1)\}$$

we see that $\{x: \mu(\{x\}) > 0\}$ is countable.

(3) We first check that if $\mu(\{a\}) = \mu(\{b\}) = 0$, $A = [a; b]$, $-\infty < x < y < \infty$, and $\alpha = (x; y)$, then

$$f(y) - f(x) \geq \mu(\alpha \cap A) + \mu(\alpha \sim A).$$

Indeed, suppose $a \leq x \leq b \leq y$. Then $\alpha \sim A = (b; y)$ and $\alpha \cap A = (x; b]$ so that, since $\mu((x; b]) = \mu((x; b))$, we have

$$\mu(\alpha \sim A) + \mu(\alpha \cap A) \leq (f(y) - f(b)) + (f(b) - f(x)) = f(y) - f(x).$$

Similarly, if $x \leq a \leq y \leq b$. If $x \leq a \leq b \leq y$, then

$$\alpha \sim A = (x; a) \cup (b; y), \quad \alpha \cap A = [a; b], \quad \mu([a; b]) = \mu((a; b))$$

and

$$\begin{aligned}\mu(\alpha \sim A) + \mu(\alpha \cap A) &\leq (f(a) - f(x) + f(y) - f(b)) + (f(b) - f(a)) \\ &= f(y) - f(x).\end{aligned}$$

Now, given $T \subset \mathscr{R}$ and $\epsilon > 0$, there exist $x_n < y_n$ and $\alpha_n = (x_n; y_n)$ so that $T \subset \bigcup_{n\in\omega} \alpha_n$ and

$$\sum_{n\in\omega} (f(y_n) - f(x_n)) \leq \mu(T) + \epsilon.$$

Since $T \cap A \subset \bigcup_{n\in\omega} (\alpha_n \cap A)$ and $T \sim A \subset \bigcup_{n\in\omega} (\alpha_n \sim A)$, we have

$$\begin{aligned}\mu(T \cap A) + \mu(T \sim A) &\leq \sum_{n\in\omega} (\mu(\alpha_n \cap A) + \mu(\alpha_n \sim A)) \\ &\leq \sum_{n\in\omega} (f(y_n) - f(x_n)) \leq \mu(T) + \epsilon.\end{aligned}$$

Thus, $[a; b] \in \mathscr{M}_\mu$ when $\mu(\{a, b\}) = 0$. Now, for any $a < b$, in view of (2), we can find x_n, y_n such that

$$a < x_n < y_n < b, \qquad \mu\{x_n, y_n\} = 0 \quad \text{and} \quad (a; b) = \bigcup_{n\in\omega} [x_n; y_n].$$

Thus $(a; b) \in \mathscr{M}_\mu$. Since any open set is the union of a countable number of open intervals, we see that any open set is μ-measurable.

(4) From the definition, we clearly have

$$\mu([a; b]) \leq \bar{f}(b) - \underline{f}(a).$$

Let $-\infty < x_n < y_n < \infty$ and $[a; b] \subset \bigcup_{n\in\omega} (x_n; y_n)$. Since $[a; b]$ is compact, there exists $N \in \boldsymbol{\omega}$ such that $[a; b] \subset \bigcup_{n=0}^{N} (x_n; y_n)$. By induction on N we shall check that

$$\bar{f}(b) - \underline{f}(a) \leq \sum_{n=0}^{N} (f(y_n) - f(x_n)).$$

Indeed, the inequality clearly holds for $N = 0$. Suppose it holds for $N = k$ and let $N = k + 1$ and $b \in (x_{k+1}; y_{k+1})$. Then $[a; x_{k+1}] \subset \bigcup_{n=0}^{k} (x_n; y_n)$ and hence

$$\bar{f}(x_{k+1}) - \underline{f}(a) \leq \sum_{n=0}^{k} (f(y_n) - f(x_n)),$$

$$\bar{f}(b) - \bar{f}(x_{k+1}) \leq f(y_{k+1}) - f(x_{k+1}).$$

Adding, we get the desired inequality for $N = k + 1$. Thus, $\mu([a; b]) = \bar{f}(b) - \underline{f}(a)$. The remaining equalities follow immediately from this and the μ-measurability of finite sets.

(5) This follows immediately from theorem 5.4.2, Chapter 5.

(6) Let $A \in \mathcal{M}_\mu$, $\epsilon > 0$ and $t + \epsilon < \mu(A)$. Since $A = \bigcup_{K \in \omega} (A \cap [-K; K])$, let B be a compact interval with $\mu(A \cap B) > t + \epsilon$. By (5), let α be open, $B \sim A \subset \alpha$ and $\mu(\alpha) \leq \mu(B \sim A) + \epsilon$. If $C = B \sim \alpha$, then C is compact, $C \subset A$, and

$$\mu(C) \geq \mu(B) - \mu(\alpha) \geq \mu(B) - \mu(B \sim A) - \epsilon = \mu(B \cap A) - \epsilon > t.$$

(7) Let $g = \bar{f}$ and $\nu =$ the Lebesgue-Stieltjes outer measure generated by g. Since $\bar{g} = g$, by (4) we have

$$\mu((a; b]) = \bar{f}(b) - \bar{f}(a) = \bar{g}(b) - \bar{g}(a) = \nu((a; b]).$$

Since any open set is the union of a countable disjoint family of such half-open intervals and, by (3), these belong to $\mathcal{M}_\mu \cap \mathcal{M}_\nu$, we conclude that μ and ν agree on open sets and hence, by (5), on all subsets of $\mathcal{R}$. Similarly for $\underline{f}$. ■

We show next that some of the properties listed in the above theorem give an intrinsic characterization of a Lebesgue-Stieltjes outer measure.

2.3. Theorem. Let μ be an outer measure on $\mathcal{R}$ such that

(a) Open sets are μ-measurable,

(b) for every compact C, $\mu(C) < \infty$,

(c) for every $A \subset \mathcal{R}$,

$$\mu(A) = \inf \{\mu(\alpha); \alpha \text{ is open and } A \subset \alpha\}.$$

Then there exists a nondecreasing function f such that μ is the Lebesgue-Stieltjes outer measure generated by f.

■ **proof:** For $x \in \mathcal{R}$, let

$$f(x) = \begin{cases} \mu([0; x)) & \text{if } x \geq 0, \\ -\mu([x; 0)) & \text{if } x < 0. \end{cases}$$

Then f is clearly nondecreasing and, for $x \leq y$, $\mu([x; y)) = f(y) - f(x)$. For any $x \in \mathcal{R}$, if $a = x - 1$, then

$$\begin{aligned} f(x) - f(a) = \mu([a; x)) &= \lim_{h \to 0^+} \mu([a; x - h)) \\ &= \lim_{h \to 0^+} f(x - h) - f(a), \end{aligned}$$

so that f is continuous on the left. Hence, by 2.2.4, if ν is the Lebesgue-Stieltjes outer measure generated by f, we have

$$\mu([x; y)) = f(y) - f(x) = \nu([x; y))$$

for $x \leq y$. Therefore μ and ν agree on open intervals, hence on open sets, and, in view of 2.2.5 and condition (c), on all subsets of $\mathcal{R}$. ■

Remark. In view of 2.2.6, any outer measure on $\mathscr{R}$ satisfying conditions (a), (b), (c) of theorem 2.3 must also satisfy

(d) for any open A,

$$\mu(A) = \sup \{\mu(C); C \text{ is compact and } C \subset A\}.$$

These four conditions may be formulated in any topological space. An outer measure on such a space satisfying these four conditions is called a Radón outer measure. On the line, the net effect of theorems 2.2 and 2.3 is to show that the family of Lebesgue-Stieltjes outer measures coincides with that of Radón outer measures. In Chapter 9, we shall give another characterization of these measures in terms of linear functionals on the space of continuous functions vanishing outside a compact set, thereby establishing the fundamental connection between measure theory and functional analysis.

2.4. Exercises

1. Let $f(x) = 0$ if $x < 0$, $f(x) = 1$ if $x > 0$, and $0 \leq f(0) \leq 1$. Then the Lebesgue-Stieltjes measure generated by f is the point mass at 0 (exercise 5.5.2, Chapter 5).

2. Let $f(x) = x$ for every $x \in \mathscr{R}$ and $\boldsymbol{\lambda}$ be the Lebesgue-Stieltjes outer measure generated by f; $\boldsymbol{\lambda}$ is referred to as Lebesgue outer measure on the line and the $\boldsymbol{\lambda}$-measurable sets as the Lebesgue or Lebesgue measurable sets. Prove that:
   (a) $\boldsymbol{\lambda}$ is translation invariant, that is, if A' is a translate of A then: $\boldsymbol{\lambda}(A) = \boldsymbol{\lambda}(A')$ and $A \in \mathscr{M}_{\boldsymbol{\lambda}}$ iff $A' \in \mathscr{M}_{\boldsymbol{\lambda}}$.
   (b) For any $\epsilon > 0$ there exists $A \subset [0; 1]$ such that A is nowhere dense and $\boldsymbol{\lambda}(A) > 1 - \epsilon$.
   (c) There exists $A \subset [0; 1]$ such that A is of the first category (see 9.1, Chapter 3) and $\boldsymbol{\lambda}(A) = 1$.
   (d) If A is the Cantor set (see 7.6.3, Chapter 3), then $\boldsymbol{\lambda}(A) = 0$.
   (e) For any $A \subset [0; 1]$, A is $\boldsymbol{\lambda}$-measurable iff

   $$\boldsymbol{\lambda}(A) = \sup \{\boldsymbol{\lambda}(C); C \text{ is closed and } C \subset A\}.$$

   (f) For any $A \subset [0; 1]$, A is $\boldsymbol{\lambda}$-measurable iff

   $$\boldsymbol{\lambda}(A) + \boldsymbol{\lambda}([0; 1] \sim A) = 1.$$

3. Let f be nondecreasing and continuous on $\mathscr{R}$, μ be the Lebesgue-Stieltjes outer measure generated by f, and $\boldsymbol{\lambda}$ be Lebesgue outer measure on the line (exercise (2) above). Show that for any $A \subset \mathscr{R}$, $\mu(A) = \boldsymbol{\lambda}(f[A])$.

4. Let μ be a Lebesgue-Stieltjes outer measure on $\mathscr{R}$ and $A \subset \mathscr{R}$. Then $A \in \mathscr{M}_\mu$ iff, for every $\epsilon > 0$, there exists a perfect set $C \subset A$ with $\mu(A \sim C) < \epsilon$.

5. Let μ, ν be Lebesgue-Stieltjes outer measures on the line. Show that if $\mu \leq \nu$ then $\mathscr{M}_\nu \subset \mathscr{M}_\mu$.
6. Let $\boldsymbol{\lambda}$ be Lebesgue outer measure on the line (exercise (2) above) and $\mathscr{G}$ be the family of open sets on the line. Show that $\mathscr{M}_\lambda \neq$ Borel field $\mathscr{G}$.
7. For each $x \in [0; 1]$, let $\bar{x} = \{t \in [0; 1]: x - t \text{ is rational}\}$. Then for $x, y \in [0; 1]$, we have either $\bar{x} = \bar{y}$ or $\bar{x} \cap \bar{y} = \phi$. Let A be the set formed by picking one point from each $\bar{x}$. Check that $A \notin \mathscr{M}_\lambda$, where $\boldsymbol{\lambda}$ is Lebesgue outer measure on the line (exercise (2) above).
(*Hint:* consider translates of A by rational numbers in $[-1, 1]$ and evaluate the measure of their union.)

3. LEBESGUE MEASURE ON $\mathscr{R}^n$

In this section we introduce Lebesgue measure on $\mathscr{R}^n$ for any $n \in \boldsymbol{\omega}_+$. This measure extends the notion of n-dimensional content from elementary geometric figures to a very wide family of sets. The passage from the line to higher dimensional Euclidean space is conceptually quite simple, since it only involves replacing intervals and their length by n-dimensional rectangles and the product of their sides in the basic process for generating an outer measure. The computations involved in checking properties of the measure are now somewhat more complex. By using induction, we reduce the problem to consideration of the Cartesian product of two spaces ($\mathscr{R}^{n-1}$ and $\mathscr{R}$) on each of which a measure is given. The techniques we use are intended to avoid as much as possible messy computations. They make limited use of special properties of $\mathscr{R}^n$ and many of them are applicable to more general situations involving product measures.

3.1. Definitions. Let $n \in \boldsymbol{\omega}_+$.

(1) For $a, b \in \mathscr{R}^n$:

$a \leq b$ iff $a_j \leq b_j$ for $j = 0, \cdots, n-1$;

$[a; b] = \{x \in \mathscr{R}^n: a_j \leq x_j \leq b_j \quad \text{for } j = 0, \cdots, n-1\}$;

$(a; b) = \{x \in \mathscr{R}^n: a_j < x_j < b_j \quad \text{for } j = 0, \cdots, n-1\}$;

$$\boldsymbol{\tau}_n((a; b)) = \boldsymbol{\tau}_n([a; b]) = \begin{cases} (b_0 - a_0) \cdots (b_{n-1} - a_{n-1}) & \text{if } a \leq b, \\ 0 & \text{otherwise.} \end{cases}$$

We shall call $(a; b)$ and $[a; b]$, respectively, open and closed rectangles in $\mathscr{R}^n$.

(2) $\boldsymbol{\lambda}_n$ is the Carathéodory measure on $\mathscr{R}^n$ generated by $\boldsymbol{\tau}_n$ and the family of open rectangles in $\mathscr{R}^n$; that is, it is defined, for every $A \subset \mathscr{R}^n$, by $\boldsymbol{\lambda}_n(A) = \inf \{\Sigma_{\alpha \in F}\, \boldsymbol{\tau}_n(\alpha);\ F \text{ is a countable family of open rectangles in } \mathscr{R}^n \text{ covering } A\}$.

$\boldsymbol{\lambda}_n$ is referred to as Lebesgue outer measure on $\mathscr{R}^n$.

$\boldsymbol{\lambda}_n/\mathcal{M}_{\boldsymbol{\lambda}_n}$ is referred to as Lebesgue measure on $\mathcal{R}^n$.
Elements of $\mathcal{M}_{\boldsymbol{\lambda}_n}$ are called Lebesgue measurable sets in $\mathcal{R}^n$.

The basic properties of $\boldsymbol{\lambda}_n$ are listed in theorem 3.2.

3.2. Theorems. Let $n \in \boldsymbol{\omega}_+$. Then

(1) For $a, b \in \mathcal{R}^n$, $\boldsymbol{\lambda}_n([a; b]) = \boldsymbol{\lambda}_n((a; b)) = \boldsymbol{\tau}_n((a; b))$.
(2) Open sets are $\boldsymbol{\lambda}_n$-measurable.
(3) For every $A \subset \mathcal{R}^n$,

$$\boldsymbol{\lambda}_n(A) = \inf \{\boldsymbol{\lambda}_n(\alpha); \alpha \text{ is open and } A \subset \alpha\}.$$

(4) For every $A \in \mathcal{M}_{\boldsymbol{\lambda}_n}$,

$$\boldsymbol{\lambda}_n(A) = \sup \{\boldsymbol{\lambda}_n(C); C \text{ is compact and } C \subset A\}.$$

(5) $\boldsymbol{\lambda}_n$ is translation invariant; that is, if A and A' are translates of each other, then $\boldsymbol{\lambda}_n(A) = \boldsymbol{\lambda}_n(A')$ and $A \in \mathcal{M}_{\boldsymbol{\lambda}_n}$ iff $A' \in \mathcal{M}_{\boldsymbol{\lambda}_n}$.

The proof of theorem 3.2 will be based on the following three lemmas. Note that, in case $n = 1$, the above theorem is a special case of theorem 2.2, since $\boldsymbol{\lambda}_1$ is the Lebesgue-Stieltjes outer measure generated by f, where $f(x) = x$ for $x \in \mathcal{R}$.

Lemma 1. Let C be a closed rectangle in $\mathcal{R}^n$ and F a finite family of open rectangles in $\mathcal{R}^n$ covering C. Then

$$\boldsymbol{\tau}_n(C) \leq \sum_{\alpha \in F} \boldsymbol{\tau}_n(\alpha).$$

■ **proof:** We use induction on n and the number of elements in F. In case $n = 1$, the result follows from theorem 2.2 by taking $f(x) = x$. Suppose that $n = m + 1$ and that the result holds in $\mathcal{R}^m$. Considering $\mathcal{R}^n$ as $\mathcal{R}^m \times \mathcal{R}$, let $C = A \times [s; t]$ and, for $\alpha \in F$,

$$\alpha = B_\alpha \times (x_\alpha; y_\alpha),$$

where A is a closed rectangle and the B_α are open rectangles in $\mathcal{R}^m$ and s, t, x_α, y_α are real numbers with $s < t$ and $x_\alpha < y_\alpha$. The desired result is clearly true in case F has only one element. Suppose then that F has $k + 1$ elements and that the result holds when the covering family has at most k elements. Let

$$I = \{\alpha \in F: \alpha \cap (A \times \{s\}) \neq \phi\} = \{\alpha \in F: x_\alpha < s < y_\alpha\}$$

and $J = F \sim I$. Then $I \neq \phi$ and $A \subset \bigcup_{\alpha \in I} B_\alpha$ so that by the induction hypothesis on n:

$$\boldsymbol{\tau}_m(A) \leq \sum_{\alpha \in I} \boldsymbol{\tau}_m(B_\alpha).$$

Let $z = \min \{y_\alpha; \alpha \in I\}$. Then

$$\boldsymbol{\tau}_m(A) \cdot (z - s) \leq \sum_{\alpha \in I} \boldsymbol{\tau}_m(B_\alpha) \cdot (z - x_\alpha).$$

Let
$$\alpha' = \begin{cases} \alpha & \text{if } \alpha \in J, \\ B_\alpha \times (z; y_\alpha) & \text{if } \alpha \in I. \end{cases}$$

For at least one $\alpha \in I$, $\alpha' = \phi$; hence there are at most k nonempty open rectangles α' in all and, for any $\epsilon > 0$, these cover the closed rectangle $A \times [z + \epsilon; t]$. By the induction hypothesis on k, then we have

$$\boldsymbol{\tau}_n(A \times [z + \epsilon; t]) \leq \sum_{\alpha \in F} \boldsymbol{\tau}_n(\alpha');$$

that is,

$$\boldsymbol{\tau}_m(A) \cdot (t - z - \epsilon) \leq \sum_{\alpha \in I} \boldsymbol{\tau}_m(B_\alpha) \cdot (y_\alpha - z) + \sum_{\alpha \in J} \boldsymbol{\tau}_n(\alpha).$$

Letting $\epsilon \to 0$ and adding the above inequality to (a) we get

$$\boldsymbol{\tau}_m(A) \cdot (t - s) \leq \sum_{\alpha \in I} \boldsymbol{\tau}_m(B_\alpha) \cdot (y_\alpha - x_\alpha) + \sum_{\alpha \in J} \boldsymbol{\tau}_n(\alpha).$$

Hence
$$\boldsymbol{\tau}_n(C) \leq \sum_{\alpha \in F} \boldsymbol{\tau}_n(\alpha). \blacksquare$$

Lemma 2. For $m, k \in \boldsymbol{\omega}_+$, considering $\mathscr{R}^{m+k}$ as $\mathscr{R}^m \times \mathscr{R}^k$, if A and B are bounded subsets of $\mathscr{R}^m$ and $\mathscr{R}^k$, respectively, then

$$\boldsymbol{\lambda}_{m+k}(A \times B) \leq \boldsymbol{\lambda}_m(A) \cdot \boldsymbol{\lambda}_k(B).$$

■ **proof:** Given $\epsilon > 0$, there exist countable families F and G of open rectangles in $\mathscr{R}^m$ and $\mathscr{R}^k$, respectively, such that $A \subset \bigcup F$, $B \subset \bigcup G$,

$$\sum_{\alpha \in F} \boldsymbol{\tau}_m(\alpha) < \boldsymbol{\lambda}_m(A) + \epsilon \quad \text{and} \quad \sum_{\beta \in G} \boldsymbol{\tau}_k(\beta) \leq \boldsymbol{\lambda}_k(B) + \epsilon.$$

Then $\{\alpha \times \beta; \alpha \in F \text{ and } \beta \in G\}$ is a countable family of open rectangles in $\mathscr{R}^{m+k}$ covering $A \times B$ and

$$\boldsymbol{\tau}_{m+k}(\alpha \times \beta) = \boldsymbol{\tau}_m(\alpha) \cdot \boldsymbol{\tau}_k(\beta) \quad \text{for} \quad \alpha \in F, \beta \in G.$$

Hence
$$\begin{aligned} \boldsymbol{\lambda}_{m+k}(A \times B) &\leq \sum_{\alpha \in F} \sum_{\beta \in G} \boldsymbol{\tau}_m(\alpha) \cdot \boldsymbol{\tau}_k(\beta) \\ &\leq (\boldsymbol{\lambda}_m(A) + \epsilon) \cdot (\boldsymbol{\lambda}_k(B) + \epsilon). \end{aligned}$$

Letting $\epsilon \to 0$ we get the desired result. ■

Lemma 3. If A is a closed rectangle and B an open rectangle in $\mathscr{R}^n$, then

$$\boldsymbol{\lambda}_n(B \cap A) + \boldsymbol{\lambda}_n(B \sim A) \leq \boldsymbol{\tau}_n(B).$$

■ **proof:** We use induction on n. For $n = 1$, the result follows from theorem 2.2. Suppose $n = m + 1$ and that the result holds in $\mathscr{R}^m$. Considering $\mathscr{R}^n$ as $\mathscr{R}^m \times \mathscr{R}$, let $A = \alpha \times I$ and $B = \beta \times J$, where α is a closed rectangle and β an open rectangle in $\mathscr{R}^m$, I is a closed interval and J an open interval in $\mathscr{R}$. Then

$$B \cap A = (\beta \cap \alpha) \times (J \cap I),$$
$$B \sim A = ((\beta \sim \alpha) \times J) \cup ((\beta \cap \alpha) \times (J \sim I));$$

hence, by lemma 2 and the induction hypothesis,

$$\begin{aligned}
&\boldsymbol{\lambda}_n(B \cap A) + \boldsymbol{\lambda}_n(B \sim A)\\
&\leq \boldsymbol{\lambda}_m(\beta \cap \alpha) \cdot \boldsymbol{\lambda}_1(J \cap I) + \boldsymbol{\lambda}_m(\beta \sim \alpha) \cdot \boldsymbol{\lambda}_1(J) + \boldsymbol{\lambda}_m(\beta \cap \alpha) \cdot \boldsymbol{\lambda}_1(J \sim I)\\
&= \boldsymbol{\lambda}_m(\beta \cap \alpha) \cdot \boldsymbol{\lambda}_1(J) + \boldsymbol{\lambda}_m(\beta \sim \alpha) \cdot \boldsymbol{\lambda}_1(J)\\
&\leq \boldsymbol{\tau}_m(\beta) \cdot \boldsymbol{\lambda}_1(J) = \boldsymbol{\tau}_m(\beta) \cdot \boldsymbol{\tau}_1(J) = \boldsymbol{\tau}_n(B). \ \blacksquare
\end{aligned}$$

We now give the proof of theorem 3.2.

(1) Let $a, b \in \mathscr{R}^n$, $a \leq b$. To see that $\boldsymbol{\lambda}_n([a; b]) \leq \boldsymbol{\tau}_n((a; b))$, let $\epsilon > 0$, $a'_j = a_j - \epsilon$ and $b'_j = b_j + \epsilon$ for $j = 0, \cdots, n-1$. Then $[a; b] \subset (a'; b')$; hence $\boldsymbol{\lambda}_n([a; b]) \leq \boldsymbol{\tau}_n((a'; b'))$ and, letting $\epsilon \to 0$ we get $\boldsymbol{\lambda}_n([a; b]) \leq \boldsymbol{\tau}_n((a; b))$. The reverse inequality follows from lemma 1 and the fact that any covering of $[a; b]$ by open rectangles can be reduced to a finite subcovering. Thus, $\boldsymbol{\lambda}_n([a; b]) = \boldsymbol{\tau}_n((a; b))$. From this it follows that $\boldsymbol{\lambda}_n([a, b]) = \boldsymbol{\lambda}_n((a; b))$ either by noting that degenerate rectangles and hence the boundary of $[a; b]$ have measure zero or by considering smaller closed rectangles inside $(a; b)$.

(2) To see that open sets in $\mathscr{R}^n$ are $\boldsymbol{\lambda}_n$-measurable, we need only check the measurability of rectangles, since any open set is the union of a countable family of rectangles. Let A be a closed rectangle in $\mathscr{R}^n$ and $T \subset \mathscr{R}^n$ with $\boldsymbol{\lambda}_n(T) < \infty$. Given $\epsilon > 0$, let F be a countable family of open rectangles in $\mathscr{R}^n$ covering T and such that

$$\sum_{B \in F} \boldsymbol{\tau}_n(B) < \boldsymbol{\lambda}_n(T) + \epsilon.$$

Then, using lemma 3, we have:

$$\begin{aligned}
\boldsymbol{\lambda}_n(T \cap A) + \boldsymbol{\lambda}_n(T \sim A) &\leq \sum_{B \in F} (\boldsymbol{\lambda}_n(B \cap A) + \boldsymbol{\lambda}_n(B \sim A))\\
&\leq \sum_{B \in F} \boldsymbol{\tau}_n(B) < \boldsymbol{\lambda}_n(T) + \epsilon.
\end{aligned}$$

(3) This follows immediately from theorem 5.4.2 in Chapter 5.

(4) Let $A \in \mathscr{M}_\mu$, $\epsilon > 0$, $t + \epsilon < \boldsymbol{\lambda}_n(A)$ and K be an ascending sequence of closed, hence compact rectangles in $\mathscr{R}^n$ covering $\mathscr{R}^n$. Then, for some $j \in \boldsymbol{\omega}$, $\boldsymbol{\lambda}_n(K_j \cap A) > t + \epsilon$. Let $B = K_j$. By (3), let α be open, $B \sim A \subset \alpha$, and $\boldsymbol{\lambda}_n(\alpha) \leq \boldsymbol{\lambda}_n(B \sim A) + \epsilon$. If $C = B \sim \alpha$, then C is compact, $C \subset A$ and

$$\begin{aligned}
\boldsymbol{\lambda}_n(C) \geq \boldsymbol{\lambda}_n(B) - \boldsymbol{\lambda}_n(\alpha) &\geq \boldsymbol{\lambda}_n(B) - \boldsymbol{\lambda}_n(B \sim A) - \epsilon\\
&= \boldsymbol{\lambda}_n(B \cap A) - \epsilon > t.
\end{aligned}$$

(5) This follows immediately from the fact that $\boldsymbol{\tau}_n$ is translation invariant. ■

3.3. Exercises

1. A is $\boldsymbol{\lambda}_n$-measurable iff, for every $\epsilon > 0$, there exists a closed set C such that $C \subset A$ and $\boldsymbol{\lambda}_n(A \sim C) < \epsilon$.
2. If $A, B \in \mathscr{M}_{\boldsymbol{\lambda}_1}$, then $A \times B \in \mathscr{M}_{\boldsymbol{\lambda}_2}$.
3. For any $A \subset \mathscr{R}$ and $B \subset \mathscr{R}$,

$$\boldsymbol{\lambda}_2(A \times B) = \boldsymbol{\lambda}_1(A) \cdot \boldsymbol{\lambda}_1(B).$$

4. $\boldsymbol{\lambda}_2$ is rotation invariant.
5. Let f be a continuous function on $\mathscr{R}$ to $\mathscr{R}$ so that $f \subset \mathscr{R}^2$. Check that $\boldsymbol{\lambda}_2(f) = 0$.
6. Let f be a function on $\mathscr{R}$ to $\mathscr{R}$ and, for every open interval $I \subset \mathscr{R}$, $f^{-1}[I]$ is λ_1-measurable. Then $\boldsymbol{\lambda}_2(f) = 0$.

7. INTEGRATION

1. INTRODUCTION

The ideas involved in integration bring it into contact with just about every branch of analysis and many fields outside of analysis as well. As a result, integration can be developed from any number of points of view, even at the fairly elementary level. To mention some of the more common approaches, one can introduce the integral through: area under the curve, limit of a sum, step functions, linear functionals, antiderivatives. Within each approach there are many types of integrals, the best known of which are perhaps those due to Riemann and Lebesgue. In this chapter, we shall develop the Lebesgue-Stieltjes integral, which is probably the most widely used integral these days. We try to indicate more than one point of view and how to pass from one to another. To this end, we begin with the geometrically intuitive idea of area under the curve, then interpret a rectangle as a step function and compute the area as the limit of a sum. We derive the basic properties of the integral by using the most convenient view. To keep the seemingly endless possibilities available at each step from bewildering the reader, we follow a fairly simple thread in the main text and leave examination of some of the possibilities to the exercises.

2. CONCEPTS INVOLVED IN LEBESGUE-STIELTJES INTEGRATION

In this section we collect the definitions of basic concepts involved in Lebesgue-Stieltjes integration. We state only simple lemmas about measurable functions and leave the study of properties of the integral to the following sections.

Given a real-valued function f on a space S and a measure μ on a family of subsets of S, we wish to define the integral of f with respect to μ. In the geometric view of the integral as "area under the curve," the key concept is that of "area." Since "the region under the curve" is a subset of $S \times \mathscr{R}$, this forces us to consider some kind of measure on $S \times \mathscr{R}$. In case $S = \mathscr{R}^n$

and $\mu = \boldsymbol{\lambda}_n$ for some $n \in \boldsymbol{\omega}_+$, a natural candidate for "area" is $\boldsymbol{\lambda}_{n+1}$. In the more general situation, we might consider a "product measure $\mu \times \lambda_1$." By taking advantage of the fact that the "region under the curve" is anchored on the "S-axis," we avoid the need for the full machinery of a product measure and get by with a very simple version using rectangles anchored on the "S-axis."

2.1. Preliminary definitions

For any function f with range $f \subset \overline{\mathscr{R}}$ and any set A:

(1) $f^+(x) = \max\{f(x), 0\}$,

(2) $f^-(x) = \max\{-f(x), 0\}$,

(3) $f_A(x) = \begin{cases} f(x) & \text{if} \quad x \in A \cap \text{domain } f \\ 0 & \text{if} \quad x \in \text{domain } f \sim A, \end{cases}$

(4) region under $f = \{(x, y)\colon 0 \le y \le f(x)\} \cup \{(x, y)\colon f(x) \le y \le 0\}$.

2.2. The outer integral

Given a space S and function μ on a family of subsets of S to $\overline{\mathscr{R}}_+$, let:

$$\mathfrak{A} = \text{domain } \mu,$$

$$H = \{(A \times [0; t]);\ A \in \mathfrak{A} \text{ and } 0 \le t \le \infty\},$$

$$\tau(A \times [0; t]) = \mu(A) \cdot t \qquad \text{(recall that } 0 \cdot \infty = 0\text{)},$$

and φ be the Carathéodory measure on $S \times \overline{\mathscr{R}}_+$ generated by τ and H, that is, for any $E \subset S \times \overline{\mathscr{R}}_+$,

$$\varphi(E) = \inf\left\{\sum_{\alpha \in F} \tau(\alpha);\ F \text{ is a countable subfamily of } H \text{ covering } E\right\}.$$

Then, for any function f with domain $f \subset S$ and any $A \subset S$:

$$\int^* f\, d\mu = \varphi(\text{region under } f^+) - \varphi(\text{region under } f^-)$$

(recall that $\infty - \infty$ is undefined),

$$\int_A^* f\, d\mu = \int^* f_A\, d\mu,$$

$$\int_\mu^* f(x)\, dx = \int^* f\, d\mu,$$

$$\int_{\mu;A}^* f(x)\, dx = \int_\mu^* f_A(x)\, dx.$$

We shall refer to $\int^* f\, d\mu$ as the outer or upper integral of f with respect to μ. We see that it is always well defined whenever f is a non-negative function and fails to exist only when $\int^* f^+\, d\mu = \infty = \int^* f^-\, d\mu$.

2.3. Step functions

The rectangles of the form $A \times [0; t]$ occurring in definition 2.2 suggest that we consider step functions of the form $t \cdot 1_A$ and countable combinations thereof. In the following definitions, we consider only disjoint combinations.

(1) For any family $\mathfrak{A}$ of subsets of S:

$\mathbf{SF}(\mathfrak{A}) = \{\Sigma_{n \in \omega} (t_n \cdot 1_{A_n}); t$ is a sequence in $\overline{\mathscr{R}}_+$ and A is a disjoint sequence in $\mathfrak{A}\}$.

(2) For any Carathéodory measure μ on S:

$$\mathbf{SF}_\mu = \mathbf{SF}(\mathscr{M}_\mu).$$

2.4. Partitions

The bases of the step functions occurring in definition 2.3 suggest countable decompositions of the space. This leads us to the following definitions.

(1) For any family $\mathfrak{A}$ of sets:

$\mathscr{P}(\mathfrak{A}) = \{P\colon P$ is a countable, disjoint subfamily of $\mathfrak{A}$ and $\bigcup P = \bigcup \mathfrak{A}\}$.

(2) For any Carathéodory measure μ:

$$\mathscr{P}_\mu = \mathscr{P}(\mathscr{M}_\mu).$$

2.5. Measurable functions

As we shall see (exercise 2.9.8), the outer integral fails to be additive on the very wide class of functions for which it is well defined. Here we isolate a family of functions on which it is additive.

(1) For any family $\mathfrak{A}$ of sets:

f is an $\mathfrak{A}$-measurable function, or $f(x)$ is $\mathfrak{A}$-measurable in x, iff f is a function into $\overline{\mathscr{R}}$ such that, for every interval $\alpha \subset \overline{\mathscr{R}}$, $f^{-1}[\alpha] \in \mathfrak{A}$.

(2) $$\mathbf{MF}(\mathfrak{A}) = \{f\colon f \text{ is an } \mathfrak{A}\text{-measurable function}\},$$

$$\mathbf{MF}^+(\mathfrak{A}) = \{f \in \mathbf{MF}(\mathfrak{A})\colon f \geq 0\}.$$

(3) For any Carathéodory measure μ:

$$\mathbf{MF}_\mu = \mathbf{MF}(\mathscr{M}_\mu),$$

$$\mathbf{MF}_\mu^{\ +} = \mathbf{MF}^+(\mathscr{M}_\mu).$$

2.6. The integral

$$\text{Let } \mathfrak{A}_\mu = \begin{cases} \text{domain } \mu \text{ if } \mu \text{ is a measure,} \\ \mathscr{M}_\mu \text{ if } \mu \text{ is a Carathéodory measure.} \end{cases}$$

Then:

(1) f is μ-integrable iff $f \in \mathbf{MF}(\mathfrak{A}_\mu)$ and $\int^* f\, d\mu \in \overline{\mathscr{R}}$.

(2) $$\int f\,d\mu = \begin{cases} \int^* f\,d\mu \text{ if } f \text{ is } \mu\text{-integrable,} \\ \text{undefined otherwise.} \end{cases}$$

(3) f is μ-summable iff $\int f\,d\mu \in \mathscr{R}$.

We conclude this section with a few very useful lemmas about measurable functions.

2.7. Lemma. Let $\mathfrak{A}$ be a σ-ring. Then f is an $\mathfrak{A}$-measurable function iff domain $f \in \mathfrak{A}$, range $f \subset \overline{\mathscr{R}}$ and any one of the following conditions holds:

(a) for every $t \in \mathscr{R}$, $f^{-1}[-\infty; t) \in \mathfrak{A}$;
(b) for every $t \in \mathscr{R}$, $f^{-1}[-\infty; t] \in \mathfrak{A}$;
(c) for every $t \in \mathscr{R}$, $f^{-1}(t; \infty] \in \mathfrak{A}$;
(d) for every $t \in \mathscr{R}$, $f^{-1}[t; \infty] \in \mathfrak{A}$;
(e) for every α in the Borel field generated by the open sets in $\overline{\mathscr{R}}$, $f^{-1}[\alpha] \in \mathfrak{A}$.

2.8. Lemma. Let $\mathfrak{A}$ be a σ-ring, $A \in \mathfrak{A}$ and, for every $n \in \boldsymbol{\omega}$, f_n be an $\mathfrak{A}$-measurable function. Then:

$$f_{0A},\ f_0^+,\ f_0^-,\ |f_0|,\ f_0 + f_1,\ f_0 \cdot f_1,\ 1/f_0,\ \sup\{f_n; n \in \boldsymbol{\omega}\},$$
$$\inf\{f_n; n \in \boldsymbol{\omega}\},\ \overline{\lim}_n f_n,\ \underline{\lim}_n f_n,\ \lim_n f_n,\ \sum_{n\in\omega} f_n$$

are all $\mathfrak{A}$-measurable functions.

■ **proof:** We only indicate some key steps in the proofs. For $t \in \mathscr{R}$:

(a) $\{x: f_0(x) + f_1(x) < t\} = \bigcup_{r \in \mathscr{R}a} (f_0^{-1}[-\infty; r) \cap f_1^{-1}[-\infty; t - r))$.
(b) If $t \geq 0$, then
$$\{x: f_0^2(x) > t\} = \{x: f_0(x) > \sqrt{t}\} \cup \{x: f_0(x) < -\sqrt{t}\}$$
and $a \cdot b = \frac{1}{4}((a + b)^2 - (a - b)^2)$ for $a, b \in \mathscr{R}$.
(c) $\{x: 1/f_0(x) < 0\} = \{x: f_0(x) < 0\}$.
For $t > 0$: $\{x: 1/f_0(x) < t\} = \{x: f_0(x) < 0\} \cup \{x: f_0(x) > 1/t\}$.
For $t < 0$: $\{x: 1/f_0(x) < t\} = \{x: f_0(x) < 0\} \cap \{x: f_0(x) > 1/t\}$.
(d) $\{x: \sup_{n\in\omega} f_n(x) \leq t\} = \bigcap_{n\in\omega} \{x: f_n(x) \leq t\}$.
(e) $\{x: \inf_{n\in\omega} f_n(x) \geq t\} = \bigcap_{n\in\omega} \{x: f_n(x) \geq t\}$.
(f) $\{x: \overline{\lim}_n f_n(x) < t\} = \bigcup_{N\in\omega} \{x: \sup_{N \leq n\in\omega} f_n(x) < t\}$.
(g) $\{x: \underline{\lim}_n f_n(x) > t\} = \bigcup_{n\in\omega} \{x: \inf_{N \leq n\in\omega} f_n(x) > t\}$.
(h) domain $\lim_n f_n = (\{x: \overline{\lim}_n f_n(x) = \infty\} \cap \{x: \underline{\lim}_n f_n(x) = \infty\})$
$\cup (\{x: \overline{\lim}_n f_n(x) = -\infty\} \cap \{x: \underline{\lim}_n f_n(x) = -\infty\})$
$\cup \{x: \overline{\lim}_n f_n(x) - \underline{\lim}_n f_n(x) = 0\}$.
(i) $\Sigma_{n\in\omega} f_n = \Sigma_{n\in\omega} f_n^+ - \Sigma_{n\in\omega} f_n^- = \lim_N \Sigma_{n=0}^N f_n^+ - \lim_N \Sigma_{n=0}^N f_n^-$. ■

2.9. Exercises

1. Let $\mathfrak{A}$ be a family of subsets of S, μ be a nonnegative function on $\mathfrak{A}$, μ^* be the Carathéodory measure on S generated by μ and $\mathfrak{A}$, and f be any function with domain $f \subset S$ and range $f \subset \overline{\mathscr{R}}$. Check that:
   (a) $\int^* f\,d\mu = \int^* f\,d\mu^*$.
   (b) If $\mathfrak{A} \subset \mathscr{M}_{\mu*}$ and $\mu' = \mu^*/\mathscr{M}_{\mu*}$, then $\int^* f\,d\mu = \int^* f\,d\mu'$.
2. Let g be a nondecreasing function on $\mathscr{R}$ to $\mathscr{R}$, $\mathfrak{A}$ be the family of open intervals and, for $a \leq b$, let $\tau((a;b)) = g(b) - g(a)$. If μ is the Lebesgue-Stieltjes measure generated by g, then, for any function f, $\int^* f\,d\tau = \int^* f\,d\mu$ (this outer integral is usually denoted by $\int^* f\,dg$).
3. Let $n \in \boldsymbol{\omega}_+$, $S = \mathscr{R}^n$, $\mu = \boldsymbol{\lambda}_n$. Identifying $S \times \mathscr{R}$ with $\mathscr{R}^{n+1}$, check that for any function f on S to $\mathscr{R}_+$:

$$\varphi\text{ (region under } f) = \boldsymbol{\lambda}_{n+1}\text{ (region under } f),$$

   where φ is as in definition 2.2. Conclude therefore that, for any sequence f of functions on S with $0 \leq f_i \leq f_{i+1}$ for $i \in \boldsymbol{\omega}$, we have

$$\int^* \lim_i f_i\,d\mu = \lim_i \int^* f_i\,d\mu.$$

4. Let μ be a Carathéodory measure on S and f be a function on S to $\overline{\mathscr{R}}$. Prove that $f \in \mathbf{MF}_\mu{}^+$ iff, for every $\epsilon > 0$, there exists $u \in \mathbf{SF}_\mu$ with $f \leq u \leq f + \epsilon$.
5. If μ is the point mass at x, for some $x \in S$, then for any function f with $x \in$ domain $f \subset S$ to $\overline{\mathscr{R}}$, $\int f\,d\mu = f(x)$.
6. If μ is counting measure on S, then for any function f on S to $\overline{\mathscr{R}}$,

$$\int f\,d\mu = \sum_{x\in S} f(x).$$

   (Thus, the theory of unordered sums is a special aspect of Lebesgue-Stieltjes integration. The relation between unordered sums and series parallels that between the Lebesgue-Stieltjes integral and the improper Riemann integral.)
7. Let μ be an outer measure on S and, for any function f on S to $\overline{\mathscr{R}}$ and $A \subset S$, let $\bar{f}(A) = \sup f[A]$.
   (a) If $\mathscr{H} = \{P\colon P$ is a countable, disjoint family of subsets of S with $\bigcup P = S\}$, then

$$\int^* f\,d\mu = \inf\left\{\sum_{A\in P} (\bar{f}(A)\cdot\mu(A));\ P \in \mathscr{H}\right\}.$$

   (The sum $\Sigma_{A\in P}\,\bar{f}(A)\cdot\mu(A)$ is usually referred to as an upper Darboux sum.)

(b) $$\int^* f\,d\mu = \inf\left\{\sum_{A\in P}(\bar{f}(A)\cdot\mu(A));\, P\in\mathscr{P}_\mu\right\}.$$

(*Hint:* use (a) and, for any $A\subset S$, consider $\alpha,\beta,\gamma\in\mathscr{M}_\mu$ such that: $A\subset\alpha$ and $\mu(A)=\mu(\alpha)$, $\alpha\sim A\subset\beta\subset\alpha$ and $\mu(\alpha\sim A)=\mu(\beta)$, $\gamma=\alpha\sim\beta\subset A$. The complete proof is far from trivial. It is rather simple if $f\in\mathbf{MF}_\mu$.)

8. Let $S=\mathscr{R}$, $\mu=\boldsymbol{\lambda}_1$. Find bounded, nonnegative functions f, g such that $\int(f+g)\,d\mu\neq\int f\,d\mu+\int g\,d\mu$.

3. ELEMENTARY PROPERTIES OF THE INTEGRAL

We shall discuss Lebesgue-Stieltjes integration only with respect to outer measures. In view of exercise 2.9.1, this does not result in any loss of generality. On the other hand, it simplifies the work considerably and extends, without any effort, the notion of an additive integral to a much wider class of functions than one might naturally consider if one worked throughout only with a measure on a ring or σ-ring $\mathfrak{A}$.

Before examining properties of the outer integral, we introduce the following definitions.

3.1. Definitions. For μ a Carathéodory measure on S and $A\subset S$:

(1) $P(x)$ holds for μ-a.a. $x\in A$ (μ-almost all x in A) iff $\mu(\{x\in A\colon P(x)$ does not hold$\})=0$.

(2) μ is σ-finite on A iff there exists a sequence α such that, for every $n\in\boldsymbol{\omega}$, $\alpha_n\subset\alpha_{n+1}\in\mathscr{M}_\mu$, $\mu(\alpha_n)<\infty$ and $A\subset\bigcup_{n\in\omega}\alpha_n$.

We now list the main elementary properties of the outer integral.

3.2. Theorems. Let μ be an outer measure on S, f and g be nonnegative functions with domain $f\cup$ domain $g\subset S$. Then:

(1) $0\le\int^* f\,d\mu\le\infty$.
(2) If $f(x)\le g(x)$ for μ-a.a. $x\in S$, then $\int^* f\,d\mu\le\int^* g\,d\mu$.
(3) If $f(x)=g(x)$ for μ-a.a. $x\in S$, then $\int^* f\,d\mu=\int^* g\,d\mu$.
(4) If $0<c<\infty$, then $\int^*(c\cdot f)\,d\mu=c\cdot\int^* f\,d\mu$.
(5) For any $A\subset S$, $\int^* 1_A\,d\mu=\mu(A)$.
(6) $\int^* f\,d\mu=0$ iff $f(x)=0$ for μ-a.a. $x\in$ domain f.
(7) If $\int^* f\,d\mu<\infty$, then $f(x)<\infty$ for μ-a.a. $x\in$ domain f and μ is σ-finite on $\{x\colon f(x)>0\}$.
(8) For any function h with domain $h\subset S$ and range $h\subset\overline{\mathscr{R}}$:

(a) $\int^* h\,d\mu=\int^* h^+\,d\mu-\int^* h^-\,d\mu$.
(b) $\int^*|h|\,d\mu\le\int^* h^+\,d\mu+\int^* h^-\,d\mu$.
(c) If $\int^* h\,d\mu$ exists, then $|\int^* h\,d\mu|\le\int^*|h|\,d\mu$.
(d) $|\int^* h\,d\mu|<\infty$ iff $\int^*|h|\,d\mu<\infty$.
(e) If $\int^* h\,d\mu$ exists and $A\subset S$, then $\int_A^* h\,d\mu$ exists.

■ **proofs:** (1), (2), and (3) are immediate from the definitions.

(4) $\{A_i \times [0; t_i]; i \in \boldsymbol{\omega}\}$ covers $\{(x, y): 0 \leq y \leq f(x)\}$ iff $\{A_i \times [0; c \cdot t_i]; i \in \boldsymbol{\omega}\}$ covers $\{(x, y): 0 \leq y \leq c \cdot f(x)\}$.

(5) Since region under $1_A = (A \times [0; 1]) \cup ((S \sim A) \times \{0\})$, we have $\int^* 1_A \, d\mu \leq \mu(A)$. On the other hand, if $\{B_i \times [0; t_i]; i \in \boldsymbol{\omega}\}$ covers the region under 1_A and $I = \{i \in \boldsymbol{\omega}: 1 \leq t_i\}$ then, for every $x \in A$ there exists $i \in \boldsymbol{\omega}$ with $(x, 1) \in B_i \times [0; t_i]$, that is, $x \in B_i$ and $1 \leq t_i$. Thus, $A \subset \bigcup_{i \in I} B_i$ and

$$\mu(A) \leq \sum_{i \in I} \mu(B_i) \leq \sum_{i \in \boldsymbol{\omega}} \mu(B_i) \cdot t_i.$$

Taking the inf over all such coverings, we get $\mu(A) \leq \int^* 1_A \, d\mu$.

(6) Let $P_0 = \{x: f(x) > 0\}$ and, for each $n \in \boldsymbol{\omega}_+$, $P_n = \{x: f(x) > 1/n\}$, $g_n = (1/n) \cdot 1_{P_n}$. If $\int^* f \, d\mu = 0$, then, since $0 \leq g_n \leq f$, we have $\int^* g_n \, d\mu = 0$ so that $\mu(P_n) = 0$ and

$$\mu(P_0) = \mu\left(\bigcup_{n \in \boldsymbol{\omega}_+} P_n\right) \leq \sum_{n \in \boldsymbol{\omega}_+} \mu(P_n) = 0.$$

If $\mu(P_0) = 0$, then, since

$$\text{region under } f \subset (P_0 \times [0; \infty]) \cup ((S \sim P_0) \times \{0\}),$$

we have $\int^* f \, d\mu \leq \mu(P_0) \cdot \infty + \mu(S \sim P_0) \cdot 0 = 0$.

(7) Let $A_0 = \{x: f(x) = \infty\}$ and, for each $n \in \boldsymbol{\omega}_+$,

$$A_n = \{x: f(x) > 1/n\}.$$

If $\mu(A_0) > 0$, then $\infty = \infty \cdot \mu(A_0) = \int^* \infty \cdot 1_{A_0} \, d\mu \leq \int^* f \, d\mu$. For any $n \in \boldsymbol{\omega}_+$, if $\mu(A_n) = \infty$, then

$$\infty = (1/n) \cdot \mu(A_n) = \int^* (1/n) \cdot 1_{A_n} \leq \int^* f \, d\mu.$$

Thus, if $\int^* f \, d\mu < \infty$, then $\mu(A_n) < \infty$ and, since μ is an outer measure, there exist $\alpha_n \in \mathscr{M}_\mu$ with $A_n \subset \alpha_n$ so that $\mu(\alpha_n) < \infty$ and $\{x: f(x) > 0\} \subset \bigcup_{n \in \boldsymbol{\omega}} \alpha_n$.

(8) (a) This is immediate from the definition.

(b) We have $|h| = h^+ + h^-$. If $h^+(x) > 0$, then $h^-(x) = 0$, and if $h^-(x) > 0$, then $h^+(x) = 0$. Hence if H_1 and H_2 are families of basic rectangles which cover, respectively, the region under h^+ and the region under h^-, then $H_1 \cup H_2$ covers the region under $h^+ + h^-$. Thus,

$$\int^* (h^+ + h^-) \, d\mu \leq \int^* h^+ \, d\mu + \int^* h^- \, d\mu.$$

(c) If $\int^* h \, d\mu$ exists, then, since $h^+ \leq |h|$ and $h^- \leq |h|$, we have:

$$\left| \int^* h^+ \, d\mu - \int^* h^- \, d\mu \right| \leq \max\left\{\int^* h^+ \, d\mu, \int^* h^- \, d\mu\right\}$$
$$\leq \int |h| \, d\mu.$$

(d) $|\int^* h\,d\mu| < \infty$ iff ($\int^* h^+\,d\mu < \infty$ and $\int^* h^-\,d\mu < \infty$) iff $\int^* |h|\,d\mu < \infty$.

(e) If $\int^* h\,d\mu$ exists, then either $\int^* h^+\,d\mu < \infty$ or $\int^* h^-\,d\mu < \infty$; hence either $\int_A^* h^+\,d\mu < \infty$ or $\int_A^* h^-\,d\mu < \infty$. Therefore $\int_A^* h\,d\mu$ exists. ∎

We consider next properties of the integral.

3.3. Theorems. Let μ be an outer measure on S.

(1) If t is a sequence in $\overline{\mathscr{R}}_+$, A is a disjoint sequence in $\mathscr{M}_\mu$, and $f = \Sigma_{i\in\omega}\, t_i \cdot 1_{A_i}$, then

$$\int f\,d\mu = \sum_{i\in\omega} t_i \cdot \mu(A_i).$$

(2) If $f \in \mathbf{MF}_\mu{}^+$ and $S = \text{domain } f$, then

$$\int f\,d\mu = \lim_{t\to 1^+} \sum_{n=-\infty}^{\infty} t^n \cdot \mu(f^{-1}[(t^n; t^{n+1}]]) + \infty \cdot \mu(f^{-1}[\{\infty\}])$$

$$= \sup\left\{\int g\,d\mu;\ g \in \mathbf{SF}_\mu \quad\text{and}\quad g \le f\right\}$$

$$= \inf\left\{\int g\,d\mu;\ g \in \mathbf{SF}_\mu \quad\text{and}\quad f \le g\right\}$$

$$= \sup\left\{\sum_{A\in P}(\inf f[A] \cdot \mu(A));\ P \in \mathscr{P}_\mu\right\}$$

$$= \inf\left\{\sum_{A\in P}(\sup f[A] \cdot \mu(A));\ P \in \mathscr{P}_\mu\right\}.$$

(3) If $f, g \in \mathbf{MF}_\mu$, $S = \text{domain } f = \text{domain } g$ and $\int f\,d\mu + \int g\,d\mu$ exists, then

$$\int (f+g)\,d\mu = \int f\,d\mu + \int g\,d\mu.$$

∎ **proofs**

(1) Clearly, $\int f\,d\mu \le \Sigma_{i\in\omega}\, t_i\mu(A_i)$. On the other hand, if $\{B_j \times [0; c_j];\ j \in \boldsymbol{\omega}\}$ covers the region under f, let $N_i = \{j \in \boldsymbol{\omega};\ t_i \le c_j\}$ for each $i \in \boldsymbol{\omega}$. Since for each $x \in A_i$ there exists $j \in \boldsymbol{\omega}$ with $(x, t_i) \in B_j \times [0; c_j]$, that is, $x \in B_j$ and $t_i \le c_j$, we see that $A_i \subset \bigcup_{j\in N_i} B_j$. Then, making use of the properties of A in the last step below, we get:

$$\sum_{i\in\omega} t_i \cdot \mu(A_i) \le \sum_{i\in\omega}\sum_{j\in N_i} c_j \cdot \mu(A_i \cap B_j) \le \sum_{i\in\omega}\sum_{j\in\omega} c_j \cdot \mu(A_i \cap B_j)$$

$$= \sum_{j\in\omega} c_j \cdot \sum_{i\in\omega} \mu(A_i \cap B_j)$$

$$\le \sum_{j\in\omega} c_j \cdot \mu(B_j).$$

Taking the inf over such coverings, we get $\Sigma_{i\in\omega}\, t_i\mu(A_i) \le \int f\,d\mu$.

(2) Let $1 < t < \infty$, $A_n = f^{-1}[(t^n; t^{n+1}]]$ for $\pm n \in \boldsymbol{\omega}$, $A_\infty = f^{-1}[\{\infty\}]$, and

$$g_t = \sum_{n=-\infty}^{\infty} t^n \cdot \mathbf{1}_{A_n} + \infty \cdot \mathbf{1}_{A_\infty}.$$

Then $g_t \in \mathbf{SF}_\mu$ and $g_t \leq f \leq t \cdot g_t$ so that $\int g_t \, d\mu \leq \int f \, d\mu \leq t \cdot \int g_t \, d\mu$ and therefore:

$$\overline{\lim_{t\to 1^+}} \int g_t \, d\mu \leq \int f \, d\mu \leq \underline{\lim_{t\to 1^+}} \int g_t \, d\mu.$$

Hence, applying (1), we get

$$\int f \, d\mu = \lim_{t\to 1^+} \sum_{n=-\infty}^{\infty} t^n \cdot \mu(A_n) + \infty \cdot \mu(A_\infty).$$

The other equalities follow readily from the above and the fact that if $P = \{A_n; \pm n \in \boldsymbol{\omega}\} \cup \{A_\infty\} \cup \{f^{-1}[\{0\}]\}$, then $P \in \mathscr{P}_\mu$ and

$$g_t \leq \sum_{A \in P} \inf f[A] \cdot \mathbf{1}_A \leq f \leq \sum_{A \in P} \sup f[A] \cdot \mathbf{1}_A \leq t \cdot g_t.$$

(3) We first note that if $u, v \in \mathbf{SF}_\mu$ with $u = \sum_{i\in\omega} s_i \cdot \mathbf{1}_{A_i}$ and $v = \sum_{j\in\omega} t_j \cdot \mathbf{1}_{B_j}$, where s, t are sequences in $\overline{\mathscr{R}}_+$ and A, B are disjoint sequences in $\mathscr{M}_\mu$ covering S, then

$$u + v = \sum_{i\in\omega} \sum_{j\in\omega} (s_i + t_j) \cdot \mathbf{1}_{(A_i \cap B_j)}$$

so that $u + v \in \mathbf{SF}_\mu$ and

$$\begin{aligned}\int (u + v) \, d\mu &= \sum_{i\in\omega} \sum_{j\in\omega} (s_i + t_j) \cdot \mu(A_i \cap B_j) \\ &= \sum_{i\in\omega} s_i \cdot \sum_{j\in\omega} \mu(A_i \cap B_j) + \sum_{j\in\omega} t_j \cdot \sum_{i\in\omega} \mu(A_i \cap B_j) \\ &= \sum_{i\in\omega} s_i \mu(A_i) + \sum_{j\in\omega} t_j \mu(B_j) \\ &= \int u \, d\mu + \int v \, d\mu.\end{aligned}$$

Next, if $f, g \in \mathbf{MF}_\mu{}^+$ with $S = \text{domain } f = \text{domain } g$, then for $u_1, u_2, v_1, v_2 \in \mathbf{SF}_\mu$ with $u_1 \leq f \leq v_1$ and $u_2 \leq g \leq v_2$, we have:

$$\begin{aligned}\int u_1 \, d\mu + \int u_2 \, d\mu = \int (u_1 + u_2) \, d\mu &\leq \int (f + g) \, d\mu \\ &\leq \int (v_1 + v_2) \, d\mu = \int v_1 \, d\mu + \int v_2 \, d\mu.\end{aligned}$$

Taking the sup over u_1, u_2 and the inf over v_1, v_2, we conclude using (2):

$$\int f \, d\mu + \int g \, d\mu = \int (f + g) \, d\mu.$$

Finally, if $f, g \in \mathbf{MF}_\mu$ and $S = \text{domain } f = \text{domain } g$, then

$$(f+g)^+ - (f+g)^- = f + g = f^+ - f^- + g^+ - g^-$$

so that

$$(f+g)^+ + f^- + g^- = f^+ + g^+ + (f+g)^-$$

and hence

$$\int (f+g)^+ \, d\mu + \int f^- \, d\mu + \int g^- \, d\mu = \int f^+ \, d\mu + \int g^+ \, d\mu + \int (f+g)^- \, d\mu.$$

Now, if $\int f \, d\mu + \int g \, d\mu > -\infty$, then $\int f^- \, d\mu + \int g^- \, d\mu < \infty$ and, since $(f+g)^- \leq f^- + g^-$, we have $\int (f+g)^- \, d\mu < \infty$. We may therefore subtract these terms in the last equality above and get:

$$\begin{aligned}\int (f+g) \, d\mu &= \int (f+g)^+ \, d\mu - \int (f+g)^- \, d\mu \\ &= \int f^+ \, d\mu - \int f^- \, d\mu + \int g^+ \, d\mu - \int g^- \, d\mu \\ &= \int f \, d\mu + \int g \, d\mu.\end{aligned}$$

If $\int f \, d\mu + \int g \, d\mu = -\infty$, then consider $-(f+g)$. ■

3.4. Exercises

1. Let μ be an outer measure on S, $c \in \overline{\mathscr{R}}$ and f, g be functions on S to $\overline{\mathscr{R}}_+$. Then
   (a) $\int^* (c \cdot f) \, d\mu = c \cdot \int^* f \, d\mu$,
   (b) $\int^* (f+g) \, d\mu \leq \int^* f \, d\mu + \int^* g \, d\mu$.
2. Let μ be an outer measure on S, $f \in \mathbf{MF}_\mu$ and $S = \text{domain } f$. For $P, P' \in \mathscr{P}_\mu$, let P' be a refinement of P iff, for every $A' \in P'$ there exists $A \in P$ with $A' \subset A$. Prove that: $\int f \, d\mu = l \in \overline{\mathscr{R}}$ iff, for every neighborhood U of l, there exists $P \in \mathscr{P}_\mu$ such that, for every $P' \in \mathscr{P}_\mu$ which is a refinement of P and every choice function ξ on P' with $\xi_A \in A$ for $A \in P'$, we have
   $$\sum_{A \in P'} f(\xi_A) \cdot \mu(A) \in U.$$
   (This is the limit of a sum approach to the integral. The above sum is usually referred to as a Riemann sum.)
3. Let μ be an outer measure on S, T be a function on S to S', and $\nu(A) = \mu(T^{-1}[A])$ for $A \subset S'$. Check that if $f \in \mathbf{MF}_\nu$, then $(f \circ T) \in \mathbf{MF}_\mu$ and $\int f \, d\nu = \int (f \circ T) \, d\mu$.

4. Let μ be an outer measure on S. Check that for any function f on S to $\overline{\mathscr{R}}_+$:

$$\int^* f\, d\mu = \inf\left\{\int g\, d\mu;\ g \in \mathbf{SF}_\mu \quad \text{and} \quad f \leq g\right\}.$$

5. Let $S = [0; 1]$, μ be the restriction of $\boldsymbol{\lambda}_1$ to $[0; 1]$,
$H_1 = \{\Sigma_{n \in \omega} t_n \cdot 1_{A_n};\ t$ is a sequence in $\overline{\mathscr{R}}_+$ and A is a disjoint sequence of arbitrary intervals covering $S\}$,
$H_2 = \{\Sigma_{n=0}^N t_n \cdot 1_{A_n};\ N \in \boldsymbol{\omega}$, t is a sequence in $\overline{\mathscr{R}}_+$ and A is a disjoint sequence in $\mathscr{M}_\mu$ covering $S\}$,
$H_3 = \{\Sigma_{n=0}^N t_n \cdot 1_{A_n};\ N \in \boldsymbol{\omega}$, t is a sequence in $\overline{\mathscr{R}}_+$ and A is a disjoint sequence of arbitrary intervals covering $S\}$,
f be any function on S to $\overline{\mathscr{R}}_+$,
$I_i(f) = \inf\{\int g\, d\mu;\ g \in H_i \text{ and } f \leq g\}$ for $i = 1, 2, 3$.
Prove that:
   (a) If f is continuous, then $\int^* f\, d\mu = I_1(f) = I_2(f) = I_3(f)$.
   (b) If f is bounded, then $\int^* f\, d\mu = I_1(f) = I_2(f)$, but we can have $I_2(f) \neq I_3(f)$.
   (c) If f is monotone, then $\int^* f\, d\mu = I_1(f)$, but we can have $I_1(f) \neq I_2(f) \neq I_3(f)$.
   (d) Even if f is on S to $\mathscr{R}_+$, we can have

$$\int^* f\, d\mu \neq I_1(f) \neq I_2(f) \neq I_3(f).$$

(This points out some of the relations between the Lebesgue integral and the proper Riemann integral.)

6. Let $g(x) = x^3$ for $x \in \mathscr{R}$ and μ be the Lebesgue-Stieltjes outer measure generated by g. Show that for any function f:

$$\int f\, d\mu = \int_{\lambda_1} 3x^2 \cdot f(x)\, dx.$$

4. LIMIT THEOREMS

In this section we discuss the key properties of the Lebesgue-Stieltjes integral which make it so useful in analysis.

4.1. Theorems (Monotone convergence). Let μ be an outer measure on S and f be a sequence of μ-measurable functions on S to $\overline{\mathscr{R}}_+$.

(1) If, for every $n \in \boldsymbol{\omega}$, $f_n \leq f_{n+1}$, then

$$\int \lim_n f_n\, d\mu = \lim_n \int f_n\, d\mu.$$

(2)
$$\int \sum_{n \in \omega} f_n\, d\mu = \sum_{n \in \omega} \int f_n\, d\mu.$$

(3) If, for every $n \in \boldsymbol{\omega}$, $A_n \subset A_{n+1} \in \mathscr{M}_\mu$ and $B = \bigcup_{n\in\omega} A_n$, then

$$\int_B f_0 \, d\mu = \lim_n \int_{A_n} f_0 \, d\mu.$$

(4) If $P \in \mathscr{P}_\mu$, then

$$\int f_0 \, d\mu = \sum_{A \in P} \int_A f_0 \, d\mu.$$

■ **proofs**

(1) Let $g = \lim_n f_n$. Then clearly $\lim_n \int f_n \, d\mu \leq \int g \, d\mu$. On the other hand, given $s < \int g \, d\mu$, we see from 3.3.2 that we can find $k \in \boldsymbol{\omega}_+$ and $0 = r_0 < \cdots < r_{k+1} = \infty$ such that if $A_i = g^{-1}[(r_i, r_{i+1}]]$ for $i = 0, \cdots, k$, then

$$s < \sum_{i=0}^{k} r_i \cdot \mu(A_i).$$

Let $B(i, n) = A_i \cap f_n^{-1}[(r_i, r_{i+1}]]$. Then, for $i = 0, \cdots, k$ and $n \in \boldsymbol{\omega}$, we have $B(i, n) \subset B(i, n+1)$ and $\bigcup_{n\in\omega} B(i, n) = A_i$. Thus,

$$\lim_n \mu(B(i, n)) = \mu(A_i)$$

and therefore:

$$s < \sum_{i=0}^{k} r_i \cdot \mu(A_i) = \lim_n \sum_{i=0}^{k} r_i \cdot \mu(B(i, n)) \leq \lim_n \int f_n \, d\mu.$$

Thus, $\int g \, d\mu \leq \lim_n \int f_n \, d\mu$.

(2) Apply (1) to $g_N = \Sigma_{n=0}^{N} f_n$.

(3), (4) These follow immediately from (1) and (2). ■

4.2. Theorems. Let μ be an outer measure on S and f be a sequence of μ-measurable functions on S.

(1) (Fatou's lemma). If there exists $g \in \mathbf{MF}_\mu$ such that $-\infty < \int g \, d\mu$ and $g \leq f_n$ for every $n \in \boldsymbol{\omega}$, then

$$\int \underline{\lim}_n f_n \, d\mu \leq \underline{\lim}_n \int f_n \, d\mu.$$

(2) If there exists $g \in \mathbf{MF}_\mu$ such that $\int g \, d\mu < \infty$ and $f_n \leq g$ for every $n \in \boldsymbol{\omega}$, then

$$\int \overline{\lim}_n f_n \, d\mu \geq \overline{\lim}_n \int f_n \, d\mu.$$

(3) (Dominated convergence). If there exists $g \in \mathbf{MF}_\mu^+$ such that $\int g \, d\mu < \infty$ and $|f_n| \leq g$ for every $n \in \boldsymbol{\omega}$ and if $\lim_n f_n(x)$ exists for μ-a.a. $x \in S$, then

$$\int \lim_n f_n \, d\mu = \lim_n \int f_n \, d\mu.$$

■ **proofs**

(1) For each $N \in \boldsymbol{\omega}$, let $F_N = \inf\{f_n;\, N \leq n \in \boldsymbol{\omega}\}$. Then

$$F_N \leq F_{N+1}, \qquad \lim_N F_N = \underline{\lim}_n f_n,$$

and
$$\int F_N\, d\mu \leq \inf\left\{\int f_n\, d\mu;\, N \leq n \in \boldsymbol{\omega}\right\}$$

so that $\lim_N \int F_N\, d\mu \leq \underline{\lim}_n \int f_n\, d\mu$. Now, $F_N - g \geq 0$ and we may also assume that $g \leq 0$, for otherwise replace g by $-g^-$. Hence by 3.3.3 and 4.1.1 we have:

$$\int \lim_N F_N\, d\mu - \int g\, d\mu = \int \lim_N (F_N - g)\, d\mu = \lim_N \int (F_N - g)\, d\mu$$
$$= \lim_N \int F_N\, d\mu - \int g\, d\mu \leq \underline{\lim}_n \int f_n\, d\mu - \int g\, d\mu.$$

Adding $\int g\, d\mu$ to both sides, we get the desired inequality.

(2) Apply (1) to $-f$ and $-g$.

(3) Since $-g \leq f_n \leq g$, we can apply (1) and (2) to get:

$$\int \underline{\lim}_n f_n\, d\mu \leq \underline{\lim}_n \int f_n\, d\mu \leq \overline{\lim}_n \int f_n\, d\mu \leq \int \overline{\lim}_n f_n\, d\mu. \;■$$

4.3. Exercises

1. Let μ be an outer measure on S and f be any sequence of nonnegative functions on S such that $f_n \leq f_{n+1}$ for $n \in \boldsymbol{\omega}$. Prove that

$$\int^* \lim_n f_n\, d\mu = \lim_n \int^* f_n\, d\mu.$$

2. Show that the hypotheses in theorems 4.1 and 4.2 are needed even when μ is Lebesgue measure on $[0; 1]$.
3. Check that theorem 4.1 does not always hold in the case of the Riemann integral.

5. FUBINI THEOREM

In this section we study the relation between integration in the plane and iterated integration on the line. We state the basic theorems only for $\boldsymbol{\lambda}_2$. However, the ideas apply equally well to much more general situations involving product measures. We should point out that the σ-finiteness of the measures involved plays a crucial role in the proofs of this section.

5.1. Theorem. Let $A \in \mathscr{M}_{\boldsymbol{\lambda}_2}$. Then

(1) $\mathbf{1}_A(x, y)$ is $\boldsymbol{\lambda}_1$-measurable in y for $\boldsymbol{\lambda}_1$-a.a. $x \in \mathscr{R}$.

(2) $\int_{\boldsymbol{\lambda}_1} \mathbf{1}_A(x, y)\, dy$ is $\boldsymbol{\lambda}_1$-measurable in x.

(3) $\int_{\boldsymbol{\lambda}_1} \int_{\boldsymbol{\lambda}_1} \mathbf{1}_A(x, y)\, dy\, dx = \boldsymbol{\lambda}_2(A)$.

■ **proof**

(a) Let A be a rectangle. Then the theorem holds in view of theorem 3.2.1, Chapter 6.

(b) Let $A = \bigcup_{n \in \omega} B_n$, where, for each $n \in \boldsymbol{\omega}$, B_n is a rectangle. Since the difference of two rectangles is the union of a finite number (at most 4) of disjoint rectangles, we can always express A as the union of a countable number of disjoint rectangles. So we may assume that the B_n are mutually disjoint. Then

$$\mathbf{1}_A = \sum_{n \in \omega} \mathbf{1}_{B_n}$$

so that we can apply (a) above, 2.8, and 4.1 to see that the theorem holds in this case.

(c) Let $A = \bigcap_{n \in \omega} B_n$ where, for each $n \in \boldsymbol{\omega}$, B_n is the union of a countable family of rectangles, $B_{n+1} \subset B_n$ and $\boldsymbol{\lambda}_2(B_0) < \infty$. Then $\mathbf{1}_A = \lim_n \mathbf{1}_{B_n}$ so that by (b), 2.8, and 4.2 the theorem holds in this case too.

(d) Let $\boldsymbol{\lambda}_2(A) = 0$. Then there exists B satisfying the conditions of the set "A" in (c) and such that $A \subset B$ and $\boldsymbol{\lambda}_2(B) = 0$. Since the theorem holds for B, we have $\int_{\boldsymbol{\lambda}_1} \int_{\boldsymbol{\lambda}_1} \mathbf{1}_B(x, y)\, dy\, dx = 0$. Hence

$$\int_{\boldsymbol{\lambda}_1} \mathbf{1}_B(x, y) dy = 0 \quad \text{for} \quad \boldsymbol{\lambda}_1\text{-a.a. } x \in \mathscr{R}$$

and $(\mathbf{1}_B(x, y) = 0$ for $\boldsymbol{\lambda}_1$-a.a. $y \in \mathscr{R})$ for $\boldsymbol{\lambda}_1$-a.a. $x \in \mathscr{R}$. Since $0 \leq \mathbf{1}_A \leq \mathbf{1}_B$ the above statements hold also for A and these immediately imply that the theorem holds for A.

(e) Let $A \in \mathscr{M}_{\boldsymbol{\lambda}_2}$ and $\boldsymbol{\lambda}_2(A) < \infty$. Then there exists B satisfying the conditions of the set "A" in (c) and such that $A \subset B$ and $\boldsymbol{\lambda}_2(B \sim A) = 0$. Then $\mathbf{1}_A = \mathbf{1}_B - \mathbf{1}_{B \sim A}$ so that applying (c), (d), 2.8, and 3.3.3, we see that the theorem holds in this case.

(f) Let $A \in \mathscr{M}_{\boldsymbol{\lambda}_2}$. Then there exist $B_n \in \mathscr{M}_{\boldsymbol{\lambda}_2}$ with $B_n \subset B_{n+1}$, $\boldsymbol{\lambda}_2(B_n) < \infty$ and $A = \bigcup_{n \in \omega} B_n$. Then $\mathbf{1}_A = \lim_n \mathbf{1}_{B_n}$ so that by (d), 2.8, and 4.1 the desired conclusion holds. ■

5.2. Theorem. Let f be a nonnegative $\boldsymbol{\lambda}_2$-measurable function on $\mathscr{R}^2$. Then:

(1) $f(x, y)$ is $\boldsymbol{\lambda}_1$-measurable in y for $\boldsymbol{\lambda}_1$-a.a. $x \in \mathscr{R}$.

(2) $\int_{\lambda_1} f(x, y)\, dy$ is $\boldsymbol{\lambda}_1$-measurable in x.

(3) $\int_{\lambda_1}\int_{\lambda_1} f(x, y)\, dy\, dx = \int f\, d\boldsymbol{\lambda}_2.$

■ **proof:** Let g be a sequence in $\mathbf{SF}_{\lambda_2}$ such that $0 \le g_n \le g_{n+1} \le f$ and $\lim_n g_n = f$. Then by 5.1, 2.8, and 4.1 the theorem holds for each g_n and therefore also for f. ■

5.3. Theorem (Fubini). Let f be a $\boldsymbol{\lambda}_2$-measurable function on $\mathscr{R}^2$. Then:

(1) $f(x, y)$ is $\boldsymbol{\lambda}_1$-measurable in y for $\boldsymbol{\lambda}_1$-a.a. $x \in \mathscr{R}$ and $f(x, y)$ is $\boldsymbol{\lambda}_1$-measurable in x for $\boldsymbol{\lambda}_1$-a.a. $y \in \mathscr{R}$.

(2) $\int_{\lambda_1} f(x, y)\, dy$ is $\boldsymbol{\lambda}_1$-measurable in x and $\int_{\lambda_1} f(x, y)\, dx$ is $\boldsymbol{\lambda}_1$-measurable in y.

(3) If $\int f\, d\boldsymbol{\lambda}_2$ exists, then

$$\int_{\lambda_1}\int_{\lambda_1} f(x, y)\, dy\, dx = \int f\, d\boldsymbol{\lambda}_2 = \int_{\lambda_1}\int_{\lambda_1} f(x, y)\, dx\, dy.$$

■ **proof:** Applying 5.2 to f^+ and f^-, we easily check (1) and (2) with the help of 2.8. If $\int f\, d\boldsymbol{\lambda}_2$ exists, by 5.2 and 3.3.3 we have:

$$\begin{aligned}\int f\, d\boldsymbol{\lambda}_2 &= \int f^+\, d\boldsymbol{\lambda}_2 - \int f^-\, d\boldsymbol{\lambda}_2\\ &= \int_{\lambda_1}\int_{\lambda_1} f^+(x, y)\, dy\, dx - \int_{\lambda_1}\int_{\lambda_1} f^-(x, y)\, dy\, dx\\ &= \int_{\lambda_1}\left(\int_{\lambda_1} f^+(x, y)\, dy - \int_{\lambda_1} f^-(x, y)\, dy\right) dx\\ &= \int_{\lambda_1}\int_{\lambda_1} f(x, y)\, dy\, dx. \blacksquare\end{aligned}$$

5.4. Corollaries

(1) (Cavalieri's principle). If $A, B \in \mathscr{M}_{\lambda_2}$ and $\boldsymbol{\lambda}_1(A[x]) = \boldsymbol{\lambda}_1(B[x])$ for $\boldsymbol{\lambda}_1$-a.a. $x \in \mathscr{R}$, then $\boldsymbol{\lambda}_2(A) = \boldsymbol{\lambda}_2(B)$.

(2) If $\alpha, \beta \in \mathscr{M}_{\lambda_1}$, then $\alpha \times \beta \in \mathscr{M}_{\lambda_2}$ and $\boldsymbol{\lambda}_2(\alpha \times \beta) = \boldsymbol{\lambda}_1(\alpha) \cdot \boldsymbol{\lambda}_1(\beta)$. (See exercises 3.3.2 and 3.3.3 in Chapter 6.)

5.5. Examples. The following examples show that the hypothesis of Fubini's theorem cannot be eliminated.

(1) Let

$$A = \left\{(x, y): 0 < y < \frac{1}{x}\right\},$$

$$B = \left\{(x, y): -\frac{1}{x} < y < 0\right\},$$

$$f = \mathbf{1}_A - \mathbf{1}_B.$$

Then $\int f^+ \, d\boldsymbol{\lambda}_2 = \boldsymbol{\lambda}_2(A) = \infty$ and $\int f^- \, d\boldsymbol{\lambda}_2 = \boldsymbol{\lambda}_2(B) = \infty$ so that $\int f \, d\boldsymbol{\lambda}_2$ does not exist,

$$\int_{\lambda_1}\int_{\lambda_1} f(x, y)\, dy\, dx = \int_{\lambda_1}\left(\frac{1}{x} - \frac{1}{x}\right) dx = 0,$$

$\int_{\lambda_1} f(x, y)\, dx = 1/y$ for $y \neq 0$, so that $\int_{\lambda_1}\int_{\lambda_1} f(x, y)\, dx\, dy$ does not exist.

(2) Let

$$A = \left\{(x, y): 0 < y < \frac{1}{x} \quad \text{or} \quad \frac{1}{x} < y < 0\right\},$$

$$B = \left\{(x, y): 0 < y < -\frac{1}{x} \quad \text{or} \quad -\frac{1}{x} < y < 0\right\},$$

$$f = \mathbf{1}_A - \mathbf{1}_B.$$

Then $\int f \, d\boldsymbol{\lambda}_2$ does not exist and

$$\int_{\lambda_1}\int_{\lambda_1} f(x, y)\, dy\, dx = \int_{\lambda_1}\int_{\lambda_1} f(x, y)\, dx\, dy = 0.$$

(3) Let

$$A_1 = \left\{(x, y): 1 < x < \infty \quad \text{and} \quad 0 < y < \frac{1}{x}\right\},$$

$$A_2 = \left\{(x, y): -\infty < x < -1 \quad \text{and} \quad 0 < y < \frac{1}{2\,|x|}\right\},$$

$$A_3 = \left\{(x, y): -\infty < x < -1 \quad \text{and} \quad -\frac{1}{3\,|x|} < y < 0\right\},$$

$$A_4 = \left\{(x, y): 1 < x < \infty \quad \text{and} \quad -\frac{1}{4x} < y < 0\right\},$$

$$f = \mathbf{1}_{A_1} - 2 \cdot \mathbf{1}_{A_2} + 3 \cdot \mathbf{1}_{A_3} - 4 \cdot \mathbf{1}_{A_4}.$$

Then $\int f\,d\boldsymbol{\lambda}_2$ does not exist,

$$\int_{\lambda_1}\int_{\lambda_1} f(x, y)\,dy\,dx = \int_{-\infty}^{-1}\left(-2\cdot\frac{1}{2\,|x|} + 3\cdot\frac{1}{3\,|x|}\right)dx$$

$$+\int_{1}^{\infty}\left(\frac{1}{x} - 4\cdot\frac{1}{4x}\right)dx = 0,$$

$$\int_{\lambda_1}\int_{\lambda_1} f(x, y)\,dx\,dy = \int_{-(1/3)}^{-(1/4)}\left(\int_{-(1/3|y|)}^{-1} 3\,dx\right)dy$$

$$+\int_{-(1/4)}^{0}\left[\int_{-(1/3|y|)}^{-1} 3\,dx + \int_{1}^{1/4|y|}(-4)\,dx\right]dy$$

$$+\int_{0}^{1/2}\left[\int_{-(1/2y)}^{-1}(-2)\,dx + \int_{1}^{1/y} dx\right]dy$$

$$+\int_{1/2}^{1}\left(\int_{1}^{1/y} dx\right)dy$$

$$= [\ln(4/3) - 1/4] + 1/4 + 1/2 + (\ln 2 - 1/2)$$

$$= \ln(8/3).$$

5.6. Exercises

1. Let $n \in \boldsymbol{\omega}_+$, f be a $\boldsymbol{\lambda}_n$-integrable function on $\mathscr{R}^n$. Prove that:

$$\int f\,d\boldsymbol{\lambda}_n = \int_{\lambda_1}\cdots\int_{\lambda_1} f(x_1, \cdots, x_n)\,dx_1\cdots dx_n.$$

2. Let μ, ν be outer measures on S and S' respectively with $\mu(S) + \nu(S') < \infty$, $H = \{(\alpha \times \beta);\ \alpha \in \mathscr{M}_\mu,\ \beta \in \mathscr{M}_\nu\}$, $\tau(\alpha \times \beta) = \mu(\alpha)\cdot\nu(\beta)$ for $\alpha \in \mathscr{M}_\mu$, $\beta \in \mathscr{M}_\nu$, and φ be the Carathéodory measure on $S \times S'$ generated by τ and H. Prove that:

(a) $H \subset \mathscr{M}_\varphi$.

(b) $\tau(A) = \varphi(A)$ for $A \in H$.

(c) $\varphi(A) = \int_\mu\int_\nu \mathbf{1}_A(x, y)\,dy\,dx$ for $A \in \mathscr{M}_\varphi$.

(d) If ν is Lebesgue outer measure on $[0; 1]$, then for any function f on S into $[0; 1]$, $\int^* f\,d\mu = \varphi$ (region under f).

$\left(\textit{Hint:}\quad \tau(\alpha \times \beta) = \int_\mu\int_\nu \mathbf{1}_{(\alpha\times\beta)}(x, y)\,dy\,dx = \int_\nu\int_\mu \mathbf{1}_{(\alpha\times\beta)}(x, y)\,dx\,dy.\right)$

6. CONNECTIONS WITH TOPOLOGY

One of the most important aspects of measure and integration is its intimate connection with topological notions. Some of the most fruitful and richest fields in mathematics rely heavily on the interplay between measure theory and topology, frequently, as in potential theory and in many areas of functional analysis, to the point of completely fusing the two streams. In this section we only point out very briefly, through the introduction of $\mathscr{L}_p$-spaces, convergence in measure and the Vitali-Lusin theorem, some simple basic ways in which the two fields are connected. We delay discussion of a much deeper and more significant connection until Chapter 9.

The theorems of sections 3 and 4 lead very naturally to certain function spaces and pseudonorms thereon in much the same way as uniform convergence and summation led to the vector spaces discussed in Chapter 2. The ideas and methods are so similar that we content ourselves with giving the definitions below and leave checking the basic properties to the exercises. We should point out that there are many more types of convergence involving measures and corresponding topological spaces than we indicate here. These as well as any serious study of $\mathscr{L}_p$-spaces are beyond the scope of this text.

6.1. Definitions. For any outer measure μ on a space S and $1 \leq p < \infty$:

(1) $\mathscr{L}_p^*(\mu) = \{f: f$ is a function with $f(x) \in \mathscr{R}$ for μ-a.a. $x \in S$ and $\int^* |f|^p \, d\mu < \infty\}$.

(2) The $\mathscr{L}_p^*(\mu)$-pseudonorm is the function N on $\mathscr{L}_p^*(\mu)$ defined by $N(f) = (\int^* |f|^p \, d\mu)^{1/p}$ for every $f \in \mathscr{L}_p^*(\mu)$.

(3) $\mathscr{L}_p(\mu) = \mathbf{MF}_\mu \cap \mathscr{L}_p^*(\mu)$.

(4) The $\mathscr{L}_p(\mu)$-pseudonorm is the restriction of the $\mathscr{L}_p^*(\mu)$-pseudonorm to $\mathscr{L}_p(\mu)$.

(5) $\mathscr{L}_\infty^*(\mu) = \{f: f$ is a function and, for some $M < \infty$, $|f(x)| \leq M$ for μ-a.a. $x \in S\}$.

(6) The $\mathscr{L}_\infty^*(\mu)$-pseudonorm is the function N on $\mathscr{L}_\infty^*(\mu)$ defined by $N(f) = \inf \{M \in \mathscr{R}_+ : |f(x)| \leq M$ for μ-a.a. $x \in S\}$ (also referred to as the essential sup of $|f|$).

(7) $\mathscr{L}_\infty(\mu) = \mathbf{MF}_\mu \cap \mathscr{L}_\infty^*(\mu)$.

(8) The $\mathscr{L}_\infty(\mu)$-pseudonorm is the restriction of $\mathscr{L}_\infty^*(\mu)$-pseudonorm to $\mathscr{L}_\infty(\mu)$.

Note that if μ is counting measure on $\boldsymbol{\omega}$, then $\mathscr{L}_p(\mu) = \ell_p$. Convergence in the $\mathscr{L}_1$, $\mathscr{L}_2$, $\mathscr{L}_\infty$ pseudonorms are sometimes referred to as mean, square-mean, and almost everywhere uniform convergence, respectively. We introduce next two more types of convergence which, like pointwise convergence, cannot, in general, be characterized by pseudonorms.

6.2. Definitions. For any outer measure μ on S:

(1) $g \doteq \lim_n f_n$ μ-ae (μ-almost everywhere) iff $\lim_n f_n(x) = g(x)$ for μ-a.a. $x \in S$.

(2) $g \doteq \lim_n f_n$ in (measure) μ iff, for every $\epsilon > 0$ and $\delta > 0$ there exists $N \in \boldsymbol{\omega}$ such that for every $n \in \boldsymbol{\omega}$ with $n > N$ we have

$$\mu(S \sim \{x: |f_n(x) - g(x)| < \epsilon\}) < \delta.$$

Perhaps the most natural way in which topological notions come into play in measure theory is when the underlying space for the measure is also a topological space. As we have seen in Chapter 6, this is the case for the Lebesgue-Stieltjes outer measures on the line where the open sets are not only measurable but can also be used to approximate the measure of any set from above. In such a situation, the continuous functions are clearly measurable. The following theorems indicate how close the measurable functions come to being continuous. Some simple consequences of these facts are discussed in the exercises.

6.3. Theorem. Let μ be an outer measure on a topological space S such that, for every $A \subset S$, $\mu(A) = \inf\{\mu(\alpha);\ \alpha \text{ is open and } A \subset \alpha\}$. If $\mu(S) < \infty$ and $f \in \mathbf{MF}_\mu$ with domain $f = S$, then, for every $\epsilon > 0$, there exists a closed set C such that $\mu(S \sim C) < \epsilon$ and f is continuous on C.

■ **proof:** Let $\{U_n; n \in \boldsymbol{\omega}\}$ be a base for the usual topology on $\mathscr{R}$. Given $\epsilon > 0$, for each $n \in \boldsymbol{\omega}$, let $A_n = f^{-1}[U_n]$, and then choose open α_n such that $A_n \subset \alpha_n$ and $\mu(\alpha_n) \leq \mu(A_n) + \epsilon/2^{n+2}$. Since $A_n \in \mathscr{M}_\mu$ and $\mu(A_n) < \infty$, we have $\mu(\alpha_n \sim A_n) = \mu(\alpha_n) - \mu(A_n) \leq \epsilon/2^{n+2}$. Let $B = \bigcup_{n\in\omega} (\alpha_n \sim A_n)$. Then $\mu(B) \leq \epsilon/2$ and f is continuous on $S \sim B$, since, for every $n \in \boldsymbol{\omega}$,

$$\begin{aligned}(f/(S \sim B))^{-1}[U_n] &= (S \sim B) \cap f^{-1}[U_n] \\ &= (S \sim B) \cap A_n = (S \sim B) \cap \alpha_n\end{aligned}$$

so that $(f/(S \sim B))^{-1}[U_n]$ is open in the relative topology of $S \sim B$. Now, let β be open, $B \subset \beta$, $\mu(\beta) < \epsilon$ and $C = S \sim \beta$. Then C is closed, $\mu(S \sim C) = \mu(\beta) < \epsilon$ and f is continuous on C, since $C \subset S \sim B$. ■

6.4. Theorem (Vitali-Lusin). Let μ be an outer measure on a topological space S such that open sets are μ-measurable and, for every $A \in \mathscr{M}_\mu$, $\inf\{\mu(\alpha \sim A);\ \alpha \text{ is open and } A \subset \alpha\} = 0$. For any function f on S to $\mathscr{R}$, we have $f \in \mathbf{MF}_\mu$ iff for every $\epsilon > 0$, there exists a closed set C such that $\mu(S \sim C) < \epsilon$ and f is continuous on C.

■ **proof:** If $f \in \mathbf{MF}_\mu$, the same proof as in 6.3 applies. For the converse, suppose that, for each $n \in \boldsymbol{\omega}_+$, C_n is closed, $\mu(S \sim C_n) < 1/n$, and f is continuous on C_n. Then, for any closed $\alpha \subset \mathscr{R}$, $C_n \cap f^{-1}[\alpha]$ is closed and, since $\mu(S \sim \bigcup_{n\in\omega_+} C_n) = 0$, we have

$$f^{-1}[\alpha] = \bigcup_{n\in\omega_+} (C_n \cap f^{-1}[\alpha]) \cup \left(\left(S \sim \bigcup_{n\in\omega_+} C_n\right) \cap f^{-1}[\alpha]\right) \in \mathscr{M}_\mu. \ ■$$

6.5. Exercises. Let μ be an outer measure on S.

1. For $1 \leq p \leq \infty$, $\mathscr{L}_p^*(\mu)$ is a vector space.
   (*Hint:* $|a + b|^p \leq 2^p(|a|^p + |b|^p)$.)
2. If $1 < p < \infty$, $1/p + 1/q = 1$, $f \in \mathscr{L}_q^*(\mu)$, $g \in \mathscr{L}_q^*(\mu)$, then

$$\int^* |f \cdot g| \, d\mu \leq \left(\int^* |f|^p \, d\mu\right)^{1/p} \left(\int^* |g|^q \, d\mu\right)^{1/q}.$$

   (*Hint:* $ab \leq a^p/p + b^q/q$ for $a, b \in \mathscr{R}_+$. See proof of 3.4, Chapter 2.)
3. For $1 \leq p \leq \infty$, the $\mathscr{L}_p^*$-pseudonorm is indeed a pseudonorm on $\mathscr{L}_p^*$.
4. For $1 \leq p \leq \infty$, $\mathscr{L}_p(\mu)$ is complete in the pseudometric induced by the $\mathscr{L}_p(\mu)$-pseudonorm.
   (*Hint:* For a Cauchy sequence f, $\mu(\{x \in S: |f_n(x) - f_{n+k}(x)| > \epsilon$ for some $k \in \boldsymbol{\omega}\}) < \epsilon$ for large n.)
5. Let $S = \mathscr{R}$, μ be a Lebesgue-Stieltjes outer measure on $\mathscr{R}$, $C_0 = \{f: f$ is a continuous function on $\mathscr{R}$, and there exists $M < \infty$ such that $f(x) = 0$ whenever $|x| > M\}$. Then: for $1 \leq p < \infty$, $\mathscr{L}_p(\mu) =$ closure C_0 in the $\mathscr{L}_p^*(\mu)$-pseudonorm, but $\mathscr{L}_\infty(\mu) \neq$ closure C_0 in the $\mathscr{L}_\infty$-pseudonorm.
   (*Hint:* Approximate any $f \in \mathscr{L}_p(\mu)$ first by a bounded function and then apply the Vitali-Lusin theorem 6.4 and the Tietze extension theorem 2.6.4, Chapter 4.)
6. Let $S = \mathscr{R}$, μ be a Lebesgue-Stieltjes outer measure on $\mathscr{R}$, and f be a function on $\mathscr{R}$ into $\mathscr{R}$. Prove that $f \in \mathbf{MF}_\mu$ iff there exists a sequence g of continuous functions on $\mathscr{R}$ to $\mathscr{R}$ such that $f \doteq \lim_n g_n$ μ-ae.
7. (Egoroff theorem). Let $\mu(S) < \infty$ and $g, f_n \in \mathbf{MF}_\mu$ for $n \in \boldsymbol{\omega}$. If $g \doteq \lim_n f_n$ μ-ae, then, for every $\epsilon > 0$, there exists $S' \in \mathscr{M}_\mu$ such that $\mu(S \sim S') < \epsilon$ and $\lim_n \sup \{|f_n(x) - g(x)|; x \in S'\} = 0$.
   (*Hint:* If $A(N, k) = \{x \in S: |f_n(x) - g(x)| > 1/k$ for some $n \in \boldsymbol{\omega}$, $n \geq N\}$, then, for $k \in \boldsymbol{\omega}_+$, $\mu(\bigcap_{N \in \boldsymbol{\omega}} A(N, k)) = 0$, so choose $N_k \in \boldsymbol{\omega}$ with $\mu(A(N_k, k) < \epsilon/2^{k+1})$.
8. Let $f_n, g_n, f', g' \in \mathbf{MF}_\mu$, $f' \doteq \lim_n f_n$ in μ and $g' \doteq \lim_n g_n$ in μ. Then
   (a) $f' + g' \doteq \lim_n (f_n + g_n)$ in μ,
   (b) if $\mu(S) < \infty$, then $f' \cdot g' \doteq \lim_n (f_n \cdot g_n)$ in μ.

7. BIRD'S EYE VIEW OF VARIOUS APPROACHES TO INTEGRATION

In this chapter we have developed integration by following the general Lebesgue-Stieltjes approach. We started with a set function and constructed an integral having desirable limit properties on a wide class of functions. With the help of the exercises, it should be fairly clear that the choice of area under the curve or step functions or Darboux sums or Riemann sums in the development of this integral is a rather minor technical matter involving mostly differences in terminology and emphasis. The key roles are played by the notions of measurability, measure zero, and countability.

This approach has some obvious similarities with the classical Riemann approach where intervals and finite operations play important roles (see exercise 3.4.5). As a matter of fact, on a bounded interval on the line, the Lebesgue integral generalizes the *proper* Riemann integral. This can be checked with the help of the following theorem due to Riemann and the fact that $\mathbf{1}_A$, where $A = \mathscr{R}a \cap [0; 1]$, is a Lebesgue, but not Riemann integrable function.

Theorem. A bounded function on a bounded interval is Riemann integrable iff it is continuous almost everywhere.

On the other hand, the Lebesgue integral is not more general than the *improper* Riemann integral, as the following example shows.

Example. Let

$$f = \sum_{n \in \omega} (-1)^n \frac{1}{n+1} \mathbf{1}_{[n; n+1)}.$$

Then
$$\int_0^\infty f(x)\, dx = \lim_N \sum_{n=0}^{N} (-1)^n \frac{1}{n+1} = \log 2,$$

but $\int f\, d\boldsymbol{\lambda}_1$ does not exist, since $\int f^+ \, d\boldsymbol{\lambda}_1 = \infty = \int f^- \, d\boldsymbol{\lambda}_1$.

If we let C_0 be the family of continuous functions vanishing outside a bounded interval of the real line, we see that the Lebesgue and the Riemann integrals yield the same linear functional on C_0, as indeed do just about all definitions of integral. However, as the above examples show, the two approaches lead to extensions of this functional to different classes of functions, neither of which is included in the other.

The above observation forms the basis for the Daniell approach to integration. In this approach one starts with some basic family F of functions (such as C_0 which requires a topology or $\mathbf{SF}_\mu$ which requires a measure) and a linear functional I on F and then one tries to extend I to a larger class through limit operations suggested by the limit theorems of section 4. In this context, the characterizations of measurable or summable functions as limits of functions in $\mathbf{SF}_\mu$ (exercise 2.9.4) or in C_0 (exercise 6.5.5) assume considerable importance.

The Daniell approach seems particularly appropriate in many branches of functional analysis where one starts with some family of continuous functions on a topological space and a linear functional defined on this family. By using only limits of sequences, without the notion of a set of measure zero, one can extend this functional to a class of topologically significant functions (the so-called Baire or Borel functions). In many cases, however, this class is not large enough for one's needs. Then one tries to extend the functional further by introducing the notion of a set of measure zero. This may be done in a variety of ways, but the most honest involves producing a measure from the functional. This is the inverse problem of the one tackled in this chapter and will be considered in Chapter 9. Once an outer measure μ is found such that $F \subset \mathbf{MF}_\mu$ and $I(f) = \int f\, d\mu$ for $f \in F$, the problem of extending I to a sufficiently large class of functions is immediately solved, since the family of μ-summable functions is usually considerably larger than the family obtained from F through sequential means alone.

Thus, to a large extent, it is through the family of measurable functions that measure theory plays a significant role in what starts out to be a purely topological problem. The significance of outer measures in this context is that they enlarge this family as much as possible. Even when we already have a measure μ on a σ-ring $\mathfrak{A}$ it pays to pass to the outer measure μ^* generated by μ and $\mathfrak{A}$, since, as we have seen (exercise 2.9.1), this does not affect the integral, but may result in $\mathbf{MF}_{\mu^*}$ being considerably larger than $\mathbf{MF}(\mathfrak{A})$. Frequently the idea of the Carathéodory process is carried out not by passing from μ to μ^*, but by extending the integral from F or $\mathbf{MF}(\mathfrak{A})$ to a larger class which turns out to be $\mathbf{MF}_{\mu^*}$. The cost of working with the functions rather than with the measures may be quite high not only in terms of effort expended but also in terms of appreciation and understanding of what is going on.

Still another important approach to integration is suggested by the fundamental theorem of calculus. On the family C_0 mentioned above, the integral may be considered as an operator which is the inverse of differentiation. The Denjoy approach tries to extend the integral as an antiderivative to a wider class of functions. We shall not take up this problem, but in the next chapter we discuss some ideas of differentiation which play important roles in the Denjoy approach.

Before closing this chapter, we should mention that the integral can also be extended to functions taking their values on spaces other than the real line. Here again the approach may vary depending upon how much structure there is on the range space and upon the field of application.

8. DIFFERENTIATION

1. INTRODUCTION

In this chapter we shall consider two major approaches to differentiation: one is suggested by the definition of derivative as the limit a quotient and the other by the fundamental theorem of calculus. The first emphasizes a differentiation process itself while the second emphasizes properties of derivatives connected with integration. Our main purpose is to introduce some of the ideas involved in the two approaches and present some fundamental theorems in such a way as to illustrate basic techniques in each approach and bring out the connection between the two.

In order to appreciate the more sophisticated formulations of differentiation, consider first the Newton quotient $(f(x + h) - f(x))/h$ for a continuous monotone increasing function f on $\mathscr{R}$. This quotient can be expressed in the form $\mu(A)/\boldsymbol{\lambda}_1(A)$, where μ is the Lebesgue-Stieltjes measure generated by f, and A is the interval having x and $x + h$ as end points. The derivative of f at x is then the limit of $\mu(A)/\boldsymbol{\lambda}_1(A)$ as h tends to zero. This leads very naturally to the notion of derivative of any set function μ with respect to another ν at a point x as the limit of the ratio $\mu(A)/\nu(A)$ as "A shrinks to x." The main problem is to specify what sets A one wishes to consider and what "A shrinks to x" means. This can be done in an unlimited number of ways, even in most abstract situations, each leading to a particular differentiation process. For example, on the real line we get respectively the ordinary or right-hand or left-hand derivative at x by taking for A intervals in which either x is any end point or x is a left end point or x is a right end point.

Whatever notion of derivative one is willing to take, sooner or later one must determine its relation to integration. The formula $f(b) - f(a) = \int_a^b g(x)\, dx$ occurring in the fundamental theorem of calculus leads, by the same reasoning as in the preceding paragraph, to considering the equation $\mu(A) = \int_A g\, d\nu$ for $A \in \mathfrak{A}$, where $\mathfrak{A}$ is some family of sets contained in the domain of the set functions μ and ν. In this setting, the differentiation problem may be formulated as follows: given μ, ν, $\mathfrak{A}$, can one find a function g such that the above equality holds, and if so how is g related to the derivative of μ with respect to ν in the sense of the previous paragraph? We give an answer to the first question in Section 2, where we present the Lebesgue decomposition and Radón-Nikodym theorems. In Section 4, we give an answer to the second question only on the real line, using the standard differentiation process. In spite of the restrictions, we formulate definitions, theorems, and proofs in such a way as to indicate how one might proceed in more general situations.

2. RADÓN-NIKODYM DERIVATIVE

Given a σ-ring $\mathfrak{A}$ and measures μ, ν on $\mathfrak{A}$, we are interested in finding a function $g \in \mathbf{MF}(\mathfrak{A})$ such that

$$\mu(A) = \int_A g \, d\nu \quad \text{for every } A \in \mathfrak{A}.$$

This clearly requires that we have

$$\inf g[A] \cdot \nu(A) \leq \mu(A) \leq \sup g[A] \cdot \nu(A)$$

and suggests that g be some kind of limit of ratios $\mu(A)/\nu(A)$, that is, that we devise an appropriate differentiation process and take for g the resulting derivative of μ with respect to ν. The existence of such a process depends on being able to find, for every $t \in \mathscr{R}_+$ a set $P \in \mathfrak{A}$ such that, for every $A \in \mathfrak{A}$, $\mu(A)/\nu(A) \geq t$ if $A \subset P$ and $\mu(A)/\nu(A) \leq t$ if $A \cap P = \phi$. Such a decomposition is guaranteed by the following theorem.

2.1. Theorem (Hahn decomposition). Let $\mathfrak{A}$ be a σ-ring, $S = \bigcup \mathfrak{A}$, and φ be a σ-additive function on $\mathfrak{A}$. Then

(1) There exists $P \in \mathfrak{A}$ such that $\text{var}^+ \varphi(S) = \varphi(P)$.
(2) There exists $P \in$ field $\mathfrak{A}$ such that for every $A \in \mathfrak{A}$:

$$\varphi(A) \geq 0 \quad \text{if} \quad A \subset P \quad \text{and} \quad \varphi(A) \leq 0 \quad \text{if} \quad A \cap P = \phi$$

so that $\text{var}^+ \varphi(A) = \varphi(A \cap P)$ and $\text{var}^- \varphi(A) = -\varphi(A \sim P)$.
If $\text{var}^+ \varphi(S) < \infty$, then $P \in \mathfrak{A}$.

■ **proof:** Recalling definition 4.1, Chapter 5, of variation, for $\alpha \subset S$, let

$$\bar{\varphi}(\alpha) = \text{var}^+ \varphi(\alpha) = \sup \{\varphi(A);\, A \in \mathfrak{A} \text{ and } A \subset \alpha\}.$$

(1) (a) Suppose first that $\bar{\varphi}(S) = t < \infty$. Then $t \geq 0$ and, for every $n \in \boldsymbol{\omega}$, there exists $A_n \in \mathfrak{A}$ such that $A_n \subset S$ and $\varphi(A_n) > t - 1/2^n$.

Let
$$P = \bigcup_{N \in \omega} \bigcap_{N \leq n \in \omega} A_n.$$

Now, for every $\alpha \in \mathfrak{A}$ with $\alpha \subset S \sim A_n$, we have $\varphi(\alpha) < 1/2^n$ and hence:

$$\varphi\left(A_N \sim \bigcap_{N \leq n \in \omega} A_n\right) = \sum_{k \in \omega} \varphi(A_N \cap \cdots \cap A_{N+k} \sim A_{N+k+1})$$
$$< \sum_{k \in \omega} \frac{1}{2^{N+k+1}} = \frac{1}{2^N}.$$

Therefore:

$$\varphi\left(\bigcap_{N \leq n \in \omega} A_n\right) = \varphi(A_N) - \varphi\left(A_N \sim \bigcap_{N \leq n \in \omega} A_n\right) > t - \frac{1}{2^{N-1}}$$

so that, by 3.6.1, Chapter 5, $\varphi(P) = t$.

(b) Suppose next that $\bar{\varphi}(S) = \infty$. If there exists $K < \infty$ such that, for every $A \in \mathfrak{A}$ with $\varphi(A) > K$, we have $\bar{\varphi}(A) = \infty$, then by recursion there is a sequence A in $\mathfrak{A}$ such that, for every $n \in \boldsymbol{\omega}$, $A_{n+1} \subset A_n$ and $\varphi(A_n) > n + K$. Then either $\varphi(A_n) = \infty$ for some $n \in \boldsymbol{\omega}$ or, by 3.6.2, $\varphi(\bigcap_{n \in \omega} A_n) = \infty$. If, for every $n \in \boldsymbol{\omega}$, there exists $A \in \mathfrak{A}$ with $\varphi(A) > n$ and $\bar{\varphi}(A) < \infty$, then by recursion there exist $A_n, B_n \in \mathfrak{A}$ such that $B_n = \bigcup_{k=0}^{n} A_k$, $\bar{\varphi}(B_n) < \infty$ and $\varphi(A_{n+1}) > \bar{\varphi}(B_n) + 1$. Then

$$\varphi\left(\bigcup_{n \in \omega} A_n\right) = \varphi(A_0) + \sum_{n \in \omega} \varphi(A_{n+1} \sim B_n)$$
$$= \varphi(A_0) + \sum_{n \in \omega} (\varphi(A_{n+1}) - \varphi(A_{n+1} \cap B_n))$$
$$\geq \varphi(A_0) + \sum_{n \in \omega} (\varphi(A_{n+1}) - \bar{\varphi}(B_n)) = \infty.$$

(2) Suppose P satisfies (1), $\varphi(P) < \infty$ and $A \in \mathfrak{A}$. If $A \subset P$ and $\varphi(A) < 0$, then $\varphi(P \sim A) = \varphi(P) - \varphi(A) > \varphi(P) = \bar{\varphi}(S)$, which is impossible. If $A \cap P = \phi$ and $\varphi(A) > 0$, then again,

$$\varphi(A \cup P) = \varphi(A) + \varphi(P) > \varphi(P) = \bar{\varphi}(S).$$

If, for P satisfying (1), $\varphi(P) = \infty$, then work with $-\varphi$. ∎

With the help of the Hahn decomposition theorem we are now in a position to prove the fundamental theorem of this section.

2.2. Theorem. Let $\mathfrak{A}$ be a σ-ring and μ, ν be measures on $\mathfrak{A}$ with $\nu(A) < \infty$ for every $A \in \mathfrak{A}$. Then there exists $g \in \mathbf{MF}^+(\text{field } \mathfrak{A})$ such that if $\Delta = \{x : g(x) = \infty\}$, then, for every $A \in \mathfrak{A}$:

(1) $\mu(A \sim \Delta) = \int_{A \sim \Delta} g \, d\nu,$

(2) $\mu(A \cap \Delta) \geq \int_{A \cap \Delta} g \, d\nu = \infty \cdot \nu(A \cap \Delta)$ (recall that $\infty \cdot 0 = 0$).

If $\mu(A) < \infty$ for every $A \in \mathfrak{A}$, then $g \in \mathbf{MF}^+(\mathfrak{A})$.

■ **proof:** Let $Q = \mathscr{R}a_+$ and for each $t \in Q$, since $\mu - t \cdot \nu$ is σ-additive on $\mathfrak{A}$, we can apply the Hahn decomposition theorem 2.1 and get $P_t \in$ field $\mathfrak{A}$ such that for every $A \in \mathfrak{A}$: $\mu(A) \geq t \cdot \nu(A)$ if $A \subset P_t$ and $\mu(A) \leq t \cdot \nu(A)$ if $A \cap P_t = \phi$. Let $S = \bigcup \mathfrak{A}$, g be the function on S given by

$$g = \sup \{t \cdot \mathbf{1}_{P_t};\ t \in Q\}$$

and $\Delta = \{x: g(x) = \infty\}$. Since Q is countable, we have $g \in \mathbf{MF}^+$(field $\mathfrak{A}$). We now check the following key property of g:

(a) For $0 \leq a \leq \infty$ and $\alpha \in \mathfrak{A}$, if $a \leq g(x)$ for every $x \in \alpha$, then $a \cdot \nu(\alpha) \leq \mu(\alpha)$.

To see (a), let $r < a$. Then $\alpha \subset \bigcup\{P_t;\ t \in Q \text{ and } r < t\}$ so that, if we order $\{t \in Q;\ r < t\}$ through a sequence s and let $A_n = P_{s_n} \sim \bigcup_{i=0}^{n-1} P_{s_i}$, we get $\alpha = \bigcup_{n\in\omega} (\alpha \cap A_n)$ and

$$r \cdot \nu(\alpha) = \sum_{n\in\omega} r \cdot \nu(\alpha \cap A_n) \leq \sum_{n\in\omega} s_n \cdot \nu(\alpha \cap A_n) \leq \sum_{n\in\omega} \mu(\alpha \cap A_n) = \mu(\alpha).$$

Since the inequality holds for any $r < a$, we have $a \cdot \nu(\alpha) \leq \mu(\alpha)$.

(1) Let $A \in \mathfrak{A}$, $1 < t < \infty$, $\alpha_n = \{x \in A: t^n \leq g(x) < t^{n+1}\}$ and $\beta = \{x: g(x) = 0\}$. Since $\alpha_n \cap P_{t_{n+1}} = \phi$, we see with the help of (a) that $t^n \cdot \nu(\alpha_n) \leq \mu(\alpha_n) \leq t^{n+1} \cdot \nu(\alpha_n)$. Also, for $0 < r \in Q$, $\beta \cap P_r = \phi$ so that $\mu(\beta) \leq r \cdot \nu(\beta)$. Since $\nu(\beta) < \infty$, we have $\mu(\beta) = 0$. Thus,

$$\sum_{n=-\infty}^{\infty} t^n \cdot \nu(\alpha_n) \leq \sum_{n=-\infty}^{\infty} \mu(\alpha_n) \leq t \sum_{n=-\infty}^{\infty} t^n \cdot \nu(\alpha_n).$$

By 3.3.2, Chapter 8, $\lim_{t\to 1} \Sigma_{n=-\infty}^{\infty} t^n \cdot \nu(\alpha_n) = \int_{A\sim\Delta} g\, d\nu$, while $\Sigma_{n=-\infty}^{\infty} \mu(\alpha_n) = \mu(A \sim \Delta)$, since $\mu(\beta) = 0$. Thus,

$$\mu(A \sim \Delta) = \int_{A\sim\Delta} g\, d\nu.$$

(2) This follows immediately from (a).
If $\mu(A) < \infty$ for every $A \in \mathfrak{A}$, then the $P_t \in \mathfrak{A}$ and $g \in \mathbf{MF}^+(\mathfrak{A})$. ■

The function g in theorem 2.2 is usually referred to as the Radón-Nikodym derivative of μ with respect to ν. In the proof of the theorem we did not explicitly indicate a differentiation process as described in the introduction. Such a process, however, is definitely there, partly hidden for the sake of technical simplicity. We leave an explicit description of it to exercise 2.6.

Without further conditions, the inequality in 2.2.2 may be strict. Clearly, to have $\mu(A) = \int_A g\, d\nu$ for every $A \in \mathfrak{A}$, a necessary condition is that $\mu(A) = 0$ whenever $\nu(A) = 0$. This leads us to the following definitions.

2.3. Definitions

(1) μ is absolutely continuous with respect to ν on $\mathfrak{A}$ iff $\mathfrak{A} \subset$ domain $\mu \cap$ domain ν and $\mu(A) = 0$ whenever $A \in \mathfrak{A}$ and $\nu(A) = 0$.

(2) μ is singular with respect to ν on $\mathfrak{A}$ iff $\mathfrak{A} \subset$ domain $\mu \cap$ domain ν and there exists $A \in \mathfrak{A}$ such that:
(a) $\nu(\alpha) = 0$ whenever $\alpha \in \mathfrak{A}$ and $\alpha \subset A$ and
(b) $\mu(\alpha) = 0$ whenever $\alpha \in \mathfrak{A}$ and $\alpha \cap A = \phi$.

We shall omit explicit reference to $\mathfrak{A}$ in the above definitions whenever μ, ν are measures and $\mathfrak{A} =$ domain $\mu \cap$ domain ν or whenever μ, ν are Carathéodory measures and $\mathfrak{A} = \mathcal{M}_\mu \cap \mathcal{M}_\nu$.

As immediate consequences of 2.2 we now have the following theorems.

2.4. Theorem (Lebesgue decomposition). Let $\mathfrak{A}$ be a σ-ring and μ, ν be measures on $\mathfrak{A}$ with $\mu(A) + \nu(A) < \infty$ for every $A \in \mathfrak{A}$. Then there exist unique measures μ_1 and μ_2 on $\mathfrak{A}$ such that: μ_1 is absolutely continuous with respect to ν, μ_2 is singular with respect to ν, and $\mu = \mu_1 + \mu_2$.

■ **proof:** Let g and Δ be as given in theorem 2.2. Since $\infty \cdot \nu(\Delta) \leq \mu(\Delta) < \infty$, we must have $\nu(\Delta) = 0$. For each $A \in \mathfrak{A}$, let $\mu_1(A) = \mu(A \sim \Delta)$ and $\mu_2(A) = \mu(A \cap \Delta)$. Then clearly $\mu = \mu_1 + \mu_2$, μ_2 is singular with respect to ν, and μ_1 is absolutely continuous with respect to ν, since for any $A \in \mathfrak{A}$ with $\nu(A) = 0$ we have $\int_{A\sim\Delta} g\, d\nu = 0$. To check uniqueness, let φ_1 be absolutely continuous with respect to ν, φ_2 be singular with respect to ν, and $\mu = \varphi_1 + \varphi_2$. Let $Z \in \mathfrak{A}$ be such that $\nu(Z) = 0$ and $\varphi_2(A \sim Z) = 0$ for every $A \in \mathfrak{A}$. Then $\nu(\Delta \cup Z) = 0$ so that $\mu_1(\Delta \cup Z) = \varphi_1(\Delta \cup Z) = 0$ and hence, for any $A \in \mathfrak{A}$,

$$\mu_1(A) = \mu_1(A \sim Z) = \mu(A \sim Z \sim \Delta) = \varphi_1(A \sim \Delta) = \varphi_1(A)$$

and therefore $\mu_2(A) = \varphi_2(A)$. ■

2.5. Theorem (Radón-Nikodym). Let $\mathfrak{A}$ be a σ-ring and μ, ν be measures on $\mathfrak{A}$ with $\mu(A) + \nu(A) < \infty$ for every $A \in \mathfrak{A}$. Then μ is absolutely continuous with respect to ν iff there exists $g \in \mathbf{MF}^+(\mathfrak{A})$ such that, for every $A \in \mathfrak{A}$, $\mu(A) = \int_A g\, d\nu$.

■ **proof:** If μ is absolutely continuous with respect to ν, let g and Δ be as given in theorem 2.2. Since $\infty \cdot \nu(\Delta) \leq \mu(\Delta) < \infty$, we have $\nu(\Delta) = 0$ and hence $\mu(\Delta) = 0$ so that, for any $A \in \mathfrak{A}$, $\mu(A \cap \Delta) = 0 = \int_{A\cap\Delta} g\, d\nu$. The converse is immediate from properties of the integral. ■

The Radón-Nikodym theorem is one of the major theorems in differentiation. Of its countless applications, we mention only conditional probability and the characterization of the topological duals of $\mathscr{L}_p$-spaces. These are taken up in exercises 2.6.3, 2.6.6, and 2.6.7 below.

2.6. Exercises

1. Describe explicitly a differentiation process inherent in the proof of theorem 2.2. More precisely, find a sequence P in $\mathscr{P}(\text{field } \mathfrak{A})$ such that, for every $n \in \boldsymbol{\omega}$, P_{n+1} is a refinement of P_n and, for ν-a.a. $x \in \bigcup \mathfrak{A}$, if $x \in \alpha_n \in P_n$, then $g(x) = \lim_n \mu(\alpha_n)/\nu(\alpha_n)$.

2. Let μ be a Lebesgue-Stieltjes outer measure on the line.
   (a) If μ is absolutely continuous with respect to $\boldsymbol{\lambda}_1$, then $\mathscr{M}_{\boldsymbol{\lambda}_1} \subset \mathscr{M}_\mu$.
   (b) If $\mu = \mu_1 + \mu_2$, where μ_1 is absolutely continuous with respect to $\boldsymbol{\lambda}_1$ and μ_2 is singular with respect to $\boldsymbol{\lambda}_1$, then μ_1 and μ_2 are Lebesgue-Stieltjes outer measures on the line.

3. Let $S = [0; 1]$, $\alpha = [0; \frac{1}{2}]$, $\mathfrak{A} = \{S, \alpha, S \sim \alpha, \phi\}$, $\beta = [\frac{1}{3}; \frac{3}{4}]$. For $A \in \mathfrak{A}$, let $\mu(A) = \boldsymbol{\lambda}_1(A \cap \beta)$ and $\nu(A) = \boldsymbol{\lambda}_1(A)$. Find an explicit formula for the Radón-Nikodym derivative of μ with respect to ν. (Note that $\mathbf{1}_\beta \notin \mathbf{MF}(\mathfrak{A})$. The answer should help explain why this derivative is also referred to as the conditional probability of β given $\mathfrak{A}$ and is denoted by $\boldsymbol{\lambda}_1(\beta/\mathfrak{A})$.) Extend your result to any σ-ring $\mathfrak{A} \subset \mathscr{M}_{\boldsymbol{\lambda}_1}$ with $\bigcup \mathfrak{A} = [0; 1]$ and $\beta \in \mathscr{M}_{\boldsymbol{\lambda}_1}$.

4. Extend theorems 2.2, 2.4, and 2.5 by replacing the conditions of "finiteness" on the measures by "σ-finiteness."

5. Let $S = [0; 1]$; $\mathfrak{A} = \{A \in \mathscr{M}_{\boldsymbol{\lambda}_1} : A \subset S\}$; for every $A \in \mathfrak{A}$, let $\mu(A) = \boldsymbol{\lambda}_1(A)$ and let $\nu(A) = 0$ if A is countable, $\nu(A) = \infty$ otherwise. Show that theorem 2.2 does not hold in this case; that is, there is no Radón-Nikodym derivative of μ with respect to ν.

6. Let ν be an outer measure on S with $\nu(S) < \infty$ and P be the $\mathscr{L}_1(\nu)$-pseudonorm. Referring to Section 6, Chapter 4, for the concepts involved, let $\varphi \in \mathscr{L}(P)$, that is, let φ be a continuous linear functional on $\mathscr{L}_1(\nu)$, and $\mu(A) = \varphi(\mathbf{1}_A)$ for $A \in \mathscr{M}_\nu$. Show that:
   (a) μ is σ-additive on $\mathscr{M}_\nu$ and there exist measures μ^+ and μ^- on $\mathscr{M}_\nu$ which are absolutely continuous with respect to ν and such that $\mu = \mu^+ - \mu^-$ and μ^+ is singular with respect to μ^-.
   (b) There exists a $g \in \mathbf{MF}_\nu$ such that
$$\mu(A) = \int_A g\, d\nu \qquad \text{for every } A \in \mathscr{M}_\nu,$$
$$\varphi(f) = \int f \cdot g\, d\nu \quad \text{for every } f \in \mathscr{L}_1(\nu),$$
   and $\|\varphi\|_P = \mathscr{L}_\infty(\nu)$-pseudonorm of g so that $g \in \mathscr{L}_\infty(\nu)$.

   Thus, the topological dual of $\mathscr{L}_1(\nu)$ can be identified with $L_\infty(\nu)$.

7. Let $1 < p < \infty$, $1 < q < \infty$, $1/p + 1/q = 1$, and in exercise 6 above replace "$\mathscr{L}_1(\nu)$" by "$\mathscr{L}_p(\nu)$" and "$\mathscr{L}_\infty(\nu)$" by "$\mathscr{L}_q(\nu)$."
8. Extend exercises 6 and 7 by replacing "$\nu(S) < \infty$" by "ν is σ-finite on S."
9. Let μ, ν be outer measures on S with $\mu(S) < \infty$. Prove that μ is absolutely continuous with respect to ν iff, for every $\epsilon > 0$, there exists $\delta > 0$ such that if $A \in \mathscr{M}_\mu \cap \mathscr{M}_\nu$ and $\nu(A) < \delta$, then $\mu(A) < \epsilon$.
10. Let $f(x) = x^3$ and μ be the Lebesgue-Stieltjes outer measure generated by f. Check that μ is absolutely continuous with respect to $\boldsymbol{\lambda}_1$, but, for every $n \in \boldsymbol{\omega}_+$, there exists $A_n \in \mathscr{M}_{\boldsymbol{\lambda}_1}$ with $\boldsymbol{\lambda}_1(A_n) < 1/n$ and $\mu(A_n) > n$.

3. THE VITALI COVERING THEOREM

In this section we discuss an important property possessed by certain families of closed sets in Euclidean space. As we shall see in the next section, this property guarantees that in certain circumstances the derivative of a measure exists almost everywhere and its integral yields back the measure.

3.1. Theorem (Vitali covering). Let $n \in \boldsymbol{\omega}_+$, $S \subset \mathscr{R}^n$, $0 < M < \infty$, $\nu = \boldsymbol{\lambda}_n$, and H be a family of closed subsets of $\mathscr{R}^n$ such that:
(a) for every $\alpha \in H$, $\nu(\{x\colon \text{dist}(\{x\}, \alpha) \leq 2 \cdot \text{diam}\, \alpha\}) < M \cdot \nu(\alpha)$,
(b) for every $x \in S$, $\inf\{\text{diam}\, \alpha; \alpha \in H \text{ and } x \in \alpha\} = 0$.
Then there exists a countable, disjoint $H' \subset H$ such that $\nu(S \sim \bigcup H') = 0$.

■ **proof:** Note that in view of (a), $\nu(\alpha) > 0$ for every $\alpha \in H$. Suppose first that S is bounded and let

$$F_0 = \{\alpha \in H\colon \alpha \cap S \neq \phi \quad \text{and} \quad \text{diam}\, \alpha \leq 1\}.$$

Then conditions (a) and (b) are still satisfied if we replace "H" by "F_0." Moreover, $\bigcup F_0$ is bounded so that, for any $k \in \boldsymbol{\omega}_+$, there can be at most a finite number of mutually disjoint sets $\alpha \in F_0$ with $\nu(\alpha) > 1/k$. Let

$$d_1 = \sup\{\text{diam}\, \alpha; \alpha \in F_0\} \quad \text{and} \quad F_1 = \{\alpha \in F_0\colon \text{diam}\, \alpha > \tfrac{1}{2} \cdot d_1\},$$

then choose a maximal family G_0 of mutually disjoint sets $\alpha \in F_1$ with $\nu(\alpha) > 1$. By recursion, for each $i \in \boldsymbol{\omega}_+$, choose a maximal family G_i of mutually disjoint sets $\alpha \in F_1$ with $\nu(\alpha) > 1/(i+1)$ and $\alpha \cap \bigcup G_j = \phi$ for $j = 0, \cdots, i-1$. Let $H_1 = \bigcup_{i \in \omega} G_i$. Then H_1 is a maximal, disjoint subfamily of F_1, that is, if $\alpha \in F_1 \sim H_1$, then $\alpha \cap \bigcup H_1 \neq \phi$. By recursion, for any $k \in \boldsymbol{\omega}_+$, let

$$d_{k+1} = \sup\{\text{diam}\, \alpha; \alpha \in F_0 \quad \text{and} \quad \alpha \cap \bigcup H_j = \phi \text{ for } j = 1, \cdots, k\},$$
$$F_{k+1} = \{\alpha \in F_0\colon \alpha \cap \bigcup H_j = \phi \text{ for } j = 1, \cdots, k \text{ and } \text{diam}\, \alpha > \tfrac{1}{2} \cdot d_{k+1}\},$$

and H_{k+1} be a maximal disjoint subfamily of F_{k+1}. Let

$$H' = \bigcup_{k \in \omega_+} H_k$$

so that H' is a disjoint subfamily of H. Since $\bigcup H'$ is bounded and $H' \subset \mathcal{M}_\nu$, we have $\Sigma_{\alpha \in H'} \nu(\alpha) = \nu(\bigcup H') < \infty$ so that H' is countable. To see that $\nu(S \sim \bigcup H') = 0$, let $\epsilon > 0$. Then there exists a finite $A \subset H'$ and $B = H' \sim A$ such that $\Sigma_{\beta \in B} \nu(\beta) < \epsilon$. We shall show that if $\beta^* = \{x: \text{dist}(\{x\}, \beta) \leq 2 \cdot \text{diam}\, \beta\}$, then $S \sim \bigcup H' \subset \bigcup_{\beta \in B} \beta^*$. To this end, let $x \in S \sim \bigcup H'$. Since $\bigcup A$ is closed, in view of condition (b), there exists $\alpha \in F_0$ such that $x \in \alpha$ and $\alpha \cap \bigcup A = \phi$. Since $d_{k+1} \leq \frac{1}{2} \cdot d_k$ and $\nu(\alpha) > 0$, we have $\lim_k d_k = 0$ and diam $\alpha > 0$ so that, for some $k \in \omega_+$, $d_{k+1} <$ diam $\alpha \leq d_k$. If $\alpha \in F_{k+1}$, then diam $\alpha \leq d_{k+1}$. Thus, $\alpha \notin F_{k+1}$ and hence $\alpha \cap \bigcup H_j \neq \phi$ for some $j = 1, \cdots, k$ so that there exists $\beta \in H'$ with $\alpha \cap \beta \neq \phi$ and diam $\alpha \leq 2 \cdot$ diam β. Since $\alpha \cap \bigcup A = \phi$, we have $\beta \in B$ and $x \in \alpha \subset \beta^*$. Thus, $S \sim \bigcup H' \subset \bigcup_{\beta \in B} \beta^*$ and, using condition (a),

$$\nu(S \sim \bigcup H') \leq \sum_{\beta \in B} \nu(\beta^*) \leq 2 \sum_{\beta \in B} \nu(\beta) < 2\epsilon.$$

Since ϵ is arbitrary, we conclude $\nu(S \sim \bigcup H') = 0$.

If S is not bounded, for each $k \in \omega$, let A_k be bounded, $A_k \subset A_{k+1}$, and $S = \bigcup_{k \in \omega} A_k$. Using the above, choose a finite disjoint $J_0 \subset H$ such that $\nu(A_0 \sim \bigcup J_0) < 1$ and let $G_0 = \{\alpha \in H: \alpha \cap \bigcup J_0 = \phi\}$, $B_0 = A_1 \sim \bigcup J_0$. Then conditions (a) and (b) are satisfied if we replace "S" by "B_0" and "H" by "G_0." Proceeding by recursion, we get sequences J and B such that, for every $k \in \omega$, J_k is a finite, disjoint subfamily of H, $\bigcup J_{k+1} \cap \bigcup J_i = \phi$ for $i = 0, \cdots, k$, $B_k = A_{k+1} \sim \bigcup_{i=0}^{k} \bigcup J_i$ and $\nu(B_k \sim \bigcup J_k) < 1/(k+1)$. If $H' = \bigcup_{k \in \omega} J_k$, then H' is a countable, disjoint subfamily of H and for any $j, k \in \omega$,

$$\nu(A_k \sim \bigcup H') \leq \nu(B_{k+j} \sim \bigcup J_{k+j}) < 1/(k+j+1),$$

so that $\nu(A_k \sim \bigcup H') = 0$ and hence $\nu(S \sim \bigcup H') = 0$. ∎

The above theorem can be extended to measures in metric spaces with some fairly obvious changes in its formulation suggested by even a superficial examination of the proof. We clearly used only very simple properties of Lebesgue measure and Euclidean space. The importance of this theorem and its generalizations lies in the fact that it is essentially the only means available for proving significant properties of derivatives. For this reason, families of sets for which the theorem holds have been singled out in the following definition.

3.2. Definition. For any family F of subsets of a pseudometric space S and outer measure ν on S:

F has the Vitali property with respect to ν iff, for every $A \subset S$ and $H \subset F$

with inf {diam α; $\alpha \in H$ and $x \in \alpha$} $= 0$ for $x \in A$, there exists a countable, disjoint $H' \subset H$ such that $\nu(A \sim \bigcup H') = 0$.

3.3. Exercises

1. Extend theorem 3.1 by replacing Euclidean space by a metric space and Lebesgue outer measure by an outer measure for which closed sets are measurable and bounded sets have finite measure.
2. Check that in $\mathscr{R}^n$ theorem 3.1 holds if we take for H any family of closed circles or squares which satisfies condition (b).
3. Check that the family of all closed rectangles in $\mathscr{R}^n$ does not satisfy condition (a) of 3.1. For $S = [0; 1] \times [0; 1]$ there exists a family of rectangles which satisfies condition (b), but for which theorem 3.1 does not hold. (This is rather hard to show, but it may well be worth trying for the insight into the Vitali property that one may gain.)

4. DIFFERENTIATION ON THE LINE

In this section we illustrate some of the basic ideas and techniques involved in a differentiation process. We restrict ourselves to the real line and to the process which consists in taking, for each x, closed intervals having x as an end point and letting their length go to zero. This leads to ordinary derivatives and enables us to obtain differentiation properties of the Lebesgue integral. Applications of the ideas discussed here to other situations are indicated in the exercises.

4.1. Definitions. For $x \in \mathscr{R}$:

(1) $\mathbf{I}(x) = \{\alpha$: for some $h, 0 < h < \infty$, and either $\alpha = [x; x + h]$ or $\alpha = [x - h, x]\}$.

(2) $D(x)$ is the ordinary derivative of μ at x iff $D(x) \in \overline{\mathscr{R}}$ and, for every neighborhood V of $D(x)$, there exists a neighborhood U of x such that $\mu(\alpha)/\boldsymbol{\lambda}_1(\alpha) \in V$ whenever $\alpha \in \mathbf{I}(x)$ and $\alpha \subset U$.

4.2. Theorem. Let μ be a Lebesgue-Stieltjes outer measure on $\mathscr{R}$ and, for every $x \in \mathscr{R}$, $D(x)$ be the ordinary derivative of μ at x if it exists. Then:

(1) $0 \leq D(x) < \infty$ for $\boldsymbol{\lambda}_1$-a.a. $x \in \mathscr{R}$.

(2) $D(x)$ is $\boldsymbol{\lambda}_1$-measurable in x.

(3) If μ_1 is absolutely continuous with respect to $\boldsymbol{\lambda}_1$, μ_2 is singular with respect to $\boldsymbol{\lambda}_1$ and $\mu = \mu_1 + \mu_2$ then, for any $A \in \mathscr{M}_{\boldsymbol{\lambda}_1}$,

$$\mu_1(A) = \int_{\boldsymbol{\lambda}_1;A} D(x)\, dx.$$

■ **proof:** Let $\nu = \boldsymbol{\lambda}_1$ and, by the Lebesgue decomposition theorem 2.4 (as extended in exercise 2.6.4), let μ_1 be absolutely continuous with respect to ν, μ_2 be singular with respect to ν, and $\mu = \mu_1 + \mu_2$. For

$0 < r < \infty$ let

$E_*(r) = \{x \in \mathscr{R}$: for every neighborhood U of x and $r' > r$ there exists $\alpha \in \mathbf{I}(x)$ with $\alpha \subset U$ and $\mu(\alpha)/\nu(\alpha) < r'\}$,

$E^*(r) = \{x \in \mathscr{R}$: for every neighborhood U of x and $r' < r$ there exists $\alpha \in \mathbf{I}(x)$ with $\alpha \subset U$ and $\mu(\alpha)/\nu(\alpha) > r'\}$.

We first check:

(a) If $A \subset E_*(r)$, then $\mu_1(A) \leq r \cdot \nu(A)$.
Indeed, given $\epsilon > 0$, let A' be open, $A \subset A'$ and $\nu(A') \leq \nu(A) + \epsilon$, and, for any $r' > r$, let $H = \{\alpha$: for some $x \in A$, $\alpha \in \mathbf{I}(x)$, $\alpha \subset A'$ and $\mu(\alpha) < r' \cdot \nu(\alpha)\}$. Then H satisfies the hypothesis of Vitali's covering theorem 3.1 with "S" replaced by "A" so that there is a countable, disjoint $H' \subset H$ such that $\nu(A \sim \bigcup H') = 0$. Since, by exercise 2.6.2, $\mathscr{M}_\nu \subset \mathscr{M}_{\mu_1}$, we have $\mu_1(A \sim \bigcup H') = 0$ so that

$$\mu_1(A) \leq \mu_1(\bigcup H') = \sum_{\alpha \in H'} \mu_1(\alpha) \leq r' \cdot \sum_{\alpha \in H'} \nu(\alpha) = r' \cdot \nu(\bigcup H')$$
$$\leq r' \cdot \nu(A') \leq r' \cdot \nu(A) + r' \cdot \epsilon.$$

Since $r' > r$ and $\epsilon > 0$ are arbitrary we have $\mu_1(A) \leq r \cdot \nu(A)$.

(b) If $A \subset E^*(r)$, then $\mu_1(A) \geq r \cdot \nu(A)$.
To see this, let Δ be such that $\nu(\Delta) = 0$ and $\mu_2(\mathscr{R} \sim \Delta) = 0$. Given $\epsilon > 0$, choose an open set A' with $A \sim \Delta \subset A'$ and $\mu(A') \leq \mu(A \sim \Delta) + \epsilon = \mu_1(A) + \epsilon$ and, for any $r' < r$, let $H = \{\alpha$: for some $x \in A \sim \Delta$, $\alpha \in \mathbf{I}(x)$, $\alpha \subset A'$ and $\mu(\alpha) > r' \cdot \nu(\alpha)\}$. Again H satisfies the hypothesis of Vitali's covering theorem 3.1 with "S" replaced by "$A \sim \Delta$," so there exists a countable disjoint $H' \subset H$ such that $\nu(A \sim \Delta \sim \bigcup H') = 0$ and therefore, since $\nu(\Delta) = 0$,

$$r' \cdot \nu(A) \leq r' \cdot \nu(\bigcup H') = \sum_{\alpha \in H'} r' \cdot \nu(\alpha) \leq \sum_{\alpha \in H'} \mu(\alpha) = \mu(\bigcup H') \leq \mu(A')$$
$$\leq \mu_1(A) + \epsilon.$$

Since $r' < r$ and $\epsilon > 0$ are arbitrary, we have $r \cdot \nu(A) \leq \mu_1(A)$.

We now turn to proving the various parts of the theorem.

(1) To see that $0 \leq D(x) < \infty$ for ν-a.a. $x \in \mathscr{R}$, let

$$Q = \{(r, s)\colon r, s \text{ are rational and } 0 < r < s\}$$

and, for $(r, s) \in Q$ and $n \in \boldsymbol{\omega}$, let

$$A(r, s, n) = E_*(r) \cap E^*(s) \cap [-n; n].$$

Then, using (a) and (b), we get:

$$\mu_1(A(r, s, n)) \leq r \cdot \nu(A(r, s, n)) \leq s \cdot \nu(A(r, s, n)) \leq \mu_1(A(r, s, n)) < \infty$$

and hence $\nu(A(r, s, n)) = 0$. Since

$$\{x\colon D(x) \text{ does not exist}\} = \bigcup_{n \in \omega} \bigcup_{(r,s) \in Q} A(r, s, n),$$

we see that $D(x)$ exists for ν-a.a. $x \in \mathscr{R}$. Also, if

$$B_n = \bigcap_{k\in\omega} E^*(k) \cap [-n; n],$$

then $\{x: D(x) = \infty\} \subset \bigcup_{n\in\omega} B_n$ and, by (b), $\infty \cdot \nu(B_n) \leq \mu_1(B_n) < \infty$ so that $\nu(B_n) = 0$. Thus, $0 \leq D(x) < \infty$ for ν-a.a. $x \in \mathscr{R}$.

(2) To see that $D(x)$ is ν-measurable in x, let $r > 0$, $k \in \boldsymbol{\omega}$ and

$$A = \{x: D(x) \leq r\} \cap [-k; k].$$

We need only check that $A \in \mathscr{M}_\nu$. To this end, let $A' \in \mathscr{M}_\nu \cap \mathscr{M}_\mu$ be such that $A \subset A' \subset [-k; k]$, $\nu(A) = \nu(A')$ and $\mu_1(A) = \mu_1(A')$. We shall show that $\nu(A' \sim A) = 0$. We first note that, for any $B \in \mathscr{M}_\nu \cap \mathscr{M}_\mu$ with $B \subset A'$, we have $\nu(A) = \nu(A \cap B) + \nu(A \sim B) \leq \nu(B) + \nu(A' \sim B) = \nu(A') = \nu(A)$ so that $\nu(A \cap B) = \nu(B)$ and similarly $\mu_1(A \cap B) = \mu_1(B)$. For any $n \in \boldsymbol{\omega}$, let $\beta_n = \{x \in A': D(x) > r + 1/n\}$ and choose $B \in \mathscr{M}_\nu \cap \mathscr{M}_\mu$ such that $\beta_n \subset B \subset A'$, $\nu(\beta_n) = \nu(B)$ and $\mu_1(\beta_n) = \mu_1(B)$. Then

$$\begin{aligned}\mu_1(\beta_n) &\geq \left(r + \frac{1}{n}\right) \cdot \nu(\beta_n) = \left(r + \frac{1}{n}\right) \cdot \nu(B) = \left(r + \frac{1}{n}\right) \cdot \nu(A \cap B)\\ &\geq \mu_1(A \cap B) + \frac{1}{n} \cdot \nu(A \cap B) = \mu_1(B) + \frac{1}{n} \cdot \nu(B)\\ &= \mu_1(\beta_n) + \frac{1}{n} \cdot \nu(\beta_n).\end{aligned}$$

Thus, $\nu(\beta_n) = 0$ and therefore $\nu(A' \sim A) = \lim_n \nu(\beta_n) = 0$.

(3) Let $A \in \mathscr{M}_\nu$. Then $\mu_1(A) = \int_{\nu;A} D(x)\, dx$, since for $1 < t < \infty$ and $B_n = \{x \in A: t^n \leq D(x) < t^{n+1}\}$, we have

$$\sum_{n=-\infty}^{\infty} t^n \nu(B_n) \leq \sum_{n=-\infty}^{\infty} \mu_1(B_n) \leq t \cdot \sum_{n=-\infty}^{\infty} t^n \cdot \nu(B_n),$$

$$\int_{\nu;A} D(x)\, dx = \lim_{t\to 1} \sum_{n=-\infty}^{\infty} t^n \cdot \nu(B_n),$$

and $\mu_1(\{x \in [-k; k]: D(x) = 0\}) \leq r \cdot 2k$ for any $r > 0$ and $k \in \boldsymbol{\omega}$ so that $\mu_1(\{x: D(x) = 0\}) = 0$ and $\mu_1(A) = \sum_{n=-\infty}^{\infty} \mu_1(B_n)$. ■

Thus, for Lebesgue-Stieltjes outer measures on the line, the Radón-Nikodym derivative with respect to $\boldsymbol{\lambda}_1$ can also be obtained through the ordinary process of differentiation. It may be interesting to compare the two approaches. In the first, we used the Hahn decomposition theorem to get an appropriate family of sets for a differentiation process, which automatically had the Vitali property. In the second, we used a given family of sets and applied the Vitali covering theorem to check that it had the Vitali property.

4.3. Exercises

1. Let f be a nondecreasing function on $\mathscr{R}$ to $\mathscr{R}$, and μ be the Lebesgue-Stieltjes outer measure generated by f. For every $x \in \mathscr{R}$, let

$$f'(x) = \lim_{h \to 0} \frac{f(x+h) - f(x)}{h}$$

and $D(x)$ be the ordinary derivative of μ at x. Check that:

(a) f is continuous at x iff $\mu(\{x\}) = 0$.
(b) If f is continuous at x, then $f'(x) = D(x)$, whenever either side exists.
(c) $0 \leq f'(x) = D(x) < \infty$ for $\boldsymbol{\lambda}_1$-a.a. $x \in \mathscr{R}$.
(d) μ is absolutely continuous with respect to $\boldsymbol{\lambda}_1$ iff for every $\epsilon > 0$ and $-\infty < a < b < \infty$, there exists $\delta > 0$ such that if $n \in \boldsymbol{\omega}$, $a \leq x_i < y_i \leq x_{i+1} \leq b$ for $i = 0, \cdots, n$ and $\Sigma_{i=0}^{n} (y_i - x_i) < \delta$, then $\Sigma_{i=0}^{n} (f(y_i) - f(x_i)) < \epsilon$.
(We shall say that f is absolutely continuous iff f satisfies the above condition.)
(e) If $-\infty < a < b < \infty$ and f is absolutely continuous, then

$$\int_{[a;b]} f' \, d\boldsymbol{\lambda}_1 = f(b) - f(a).$$

(f) If $g \in \mathbf{MF}^+(\boldsymbol{\lambda}_1)$, $a \in \mathscr{R}$, $f(x) = \int_{(a;x)} g \, d\boldsymbol{\lambda}_1 < \infty$ for $x \geq a$ and $f(x) = -\int_{(x;a)} g \, d\boldsymbol{\lambda}_1 < \infty$ for $x \leq a$, then f is absolutely continuous and $f'(x) = g(x)$ for $\boldsymbol{\lambda}_1$-a.a. $x \in \mathscr{R}$.
(g) μ is singular with respect to $\boldsymbol{\lambda}_1$ iff $f'(x) = 0$ for $\boldsymbol{\lambda}_1$-a.a. $x \in \mathscr{R}$.

2. Let f be the Cantor function on $[0, 1]$, that is, for any sequence a in $\{0, 2\}$:

$$f(x) = \sum_{i=0}^{n} \frac{a_i}{2^{i+2}} \quad \text{if} \quad n \in \boldsymbol{\omega} \quad \text{and} \quad 0 \leq \sum_{i=0}^{n} \frac{a_i}{3^{i+1}} - \frac{1}{3^n} \leq x \leq \sum_{i=0}^{n} \frac{a_i}{3^{i+1}}$$

$$f(x) = \sum_{i \in \boldsymbol{\omega}} \frac{a_i}{2^{i+2}} \quad \text{if} \quad x = \sum_{i \in \boldsymbol{\omega}} \frac{a_i}{3^{i+1}}.$$

Check that f is continuous and nondecreasing, $f(0) = 0$, $f(1) = 1$, $f'(x) = 0$ for $x \in [0; 1] \sim C$, where C is the Cantor set, so that $f'(x) = 0$ for $\boldsymbol{\lambda}_1$-a.a. $x \in [0; 1]$. Thus, $\int f' \, d\boldsymbol{\lambda}_1 = 0 < f(1) - f(0)$. If μ is the Lebesgue-Stieltjes outer measure generated by f, then μ is singular with respect to $\boldsymbol{\lambda}_1$.

3. Let $n \in \boldsymbol{\omega}_+$, $E \subset \mathscr{R}^n$, $\nu = \boldsymbol{\lambda}_n$, $\mu(A) = \nu(E \cap A)$ for any $A \subset \mathscr{R}^n$ and, for each $x \in \mathscr{R}^n$, let $S(x)$ be the family of closed spheres centered at x and having positive radius, and $D(x)$ be the limit of $\mu(A)/\nu(A)$ as A runs over $S(x)$ and diam A tends to zero ($D(x)$ is called the density of E at x). Check that if $E \in \mathscr{M}_\nu$, then $D(x) = 1$ for ν-a.a. $x \in E$ and $D(x) = 0$ for ν-a.a. $x \in \mathscr{R}^n \sim E$.

9. RIESZ REPRESENTATION

1. INTRODUCTION

In this chapter we concentrate on the real line and introduce three important families: **LS** consisting of signed Lebesgue-Stieltjes measures, **BV** consisting of functions of bounded variation, and $\mathbf{C}_0^*$ consisting of "continuous" linear functionals on $\mathbf{C}_0$. Our main goal is to indicate how these three families can be identified and thereby establish the fundamental bridges connecting measure theory, the classical theory of functions of a real variable, and functional analysis.

2. SIGNED MEASURES

The Jordan decomposition theorem (4.2, Chapter 5) pointed out that any σ-additive function on a ring can be expressed as the difference of two measures. As a result, we concentrated most of our attention on the study of measures. We now try to complete the picture by examining differences of measures. We restrict ourselves to differences of Lebesgue-Stieltjes measures, but these are sufficiently complex to bring out the most significant aspects of the difficulties. In the unbounded situation, one problem is how to deal with $\infty - \infty$; for example, $2\boldsymbol{\lambda}_1 - \boldsymbol{\lambda}_1$ which should be equal to $\boldsymbol{\lambda}_1$ is undefined on $(0; \infty)$. When dealing with a family of measures, another problem is to find a sufficiently large common domain. It is with these problems in mind that we introduce the definitions below.

2.1. Definitions

(1) $\mathfrak{A}_0 = \{A$: for every Lebesgue-Stieltjes outer measure μ,

$$A \in \mathcal{M}_\mu \quad \text{and} \quad \mu(A) < \infty\}.$$

(2) $\mathbf{LS} = \{\varphi$: for some Lebesgue-Stieltjes outer measures μ_1 and μ_2, $\varphi = (\mu_1 - \mu_2)/\mathfrak{A}_0\}$.

(3) $\mathbf{LS}_+ = \{\varphi \in \mathbf{LS}: \varphi(A) \geq 0$ for every $A \in \mathfrak{A}_0\}$.

(4) For any $\varphi \in \mathbf{LS}$ and function f on $\mathscr{R}$ to $\mathscr{R}$:

$$\int f\,d\varphi = \int f\,d\text{var}^+\,\varphi - \int f\,d\text{var}^-\,\varphi$$

(see 4.1, Chapter 5, for definition of variation).

Elements of $\mathfrak{A}_0$ are referred to as absolutely measurable or universally measurable sets. Clearly, the bounded Borel sets on the line belong to $\mathfrak{A}_0$, but $\mathfrak{A}_0$ also contains non-Borel sets, for example, analytic sets and complements of analytic sets (which have not been discussed in this text). Other interesting sets in $\mathfrak{A}_0$ are those A with $\mu(A) = 0$ for every continuous Lebesgue-Stieltjes outer measure μ. Surprisingly enough, there are such sets which are not countable.

Elements of **LS** are called signed Lebesgue-Stieltjes measures. Clearly, the representation of any $\varphi \in \mathbf{LS}$ as the difference of two measures is not unique. We now check that the most "efficient" representation is through $\text{var}^+\,\varphi - \text{var}^-\,\varphi$.

2.2. Theorem. Let μ_1 and μ_2 be Lebesgue-Stieltjes outer measures on $\mathscr{R}$, $\varphi = (\mu_1 - \mu_2)/\mathfrak{A}_0$, $\varphi_1 = \text{var}^+\,\varphi$ and $\varphi_2 = \text{var}^-\,\varphi$. Then:

(1) $\mathfrak{A}_0$ is a ring containing all compact sets in $\mathscr{R}$.

(2) φ is σ-additive on $\mathfrak{A}_0$.

(3) $\varphi_1 \leq \mu_1$, $\varphi_2 \leq \mu_2$, and $\varphi = (\varphi_1 - \varphi_2)/\mathfrak{A}_0$.

(4) φ_1 is singular with respect to φ_2.

(5) φ_1 and φ_2 are Lebesgue-Stieltjes outer measures on $\mathscr{R}$.

(6) $\int f\,d\varphi = \int f\,d\mu_1 - \int f\,d\mu_2$ whenever $\int f\,d\mu_1 - \int f\,d\mu_2$ exists.

■ **proofs**

(1), (2) These are immediate consequences of the definitions and properties of Lebesgue-Stieltjes outer measures.

(3) This follows from the definition of variation and the Jordan decomposition theorem 4.2, Chapter 5.

(4) By the Hahn decomposition theorem 2.1, Chapter 8, for every $n \in \boldsymbol{\omega}$, there exists $P_n \in \mathfrak{A}_0$ such that $P_n \subset [-n; n]$ and, for every $A \subset [-n; n]$, $\varphi_1(A) = \varphi(A \cap P_n)$ and $\varphi_2(A) = -\varphi(A \sim P_n)$. Let $P' = \bigcup_{n\in\omega} P_n$. Then, by 4.2.2, Chapter 5, $\varphi_1(\mathscr{R} \sim P') = 0$ and $\varphi_2(P') = 0$.

(5) For every $n \in \boldsymbol{\omega}$, the argument above shows that the restrictions of φ_1 and φ_2 to $[-n, n]$ are Lebesgue-Stieltjes outer measures. Hence, by 4.2.2, Chapter 5, φ_1 and φ_2 are Lebesgue-Stieltjes outer measures on $\mathscr{R}$.

(6) Let $\int f\,d\mu_1 - \int f\,d\mu_2$ exist. Then $f \in \mathbf{MF}_{\mu_1} \cap \mathbf{MF}_{\mu_2}$. We may suppose $f \geq 0$ and $\int f\,d\mu_2 < \infty$. Since $\varphi_1 \leq \mu_1$ and $\varphi_2 \leq \mu_2$, we have, by exercise 2.4.5, Chapter 6, $\mathscr{M}_{\mu_1} \subset \mathscr{M}_{\varphi_1}$, $\mathscr{M}_{\mu_2} \subset \mathscr{M}_{\varphi_2}$, and $\int f\,d\varphi_2 \leq \int f\,d\mu_2 < \infty$. Thus, $f \in \mathbf{MF}_{\varphi_1} \cap \mathbf{MF}_{\varphi_2}$ and $\int f\,d\varphi_1 - \int f\,d\varphi_2$ exists. By (3), $(\mu_1 + \varphi_2)(A) = (\varphi_1 + \mu_2)(A)$ for all $A \in \mathfrak{A}_0$, hence also for all $A \subset \mathscr{R}$ and $\int f\,d\mu_1 + \int f\,d\varphi_2 = \int f\,d\varphi_1 + \int f\,d\mu_2$. Subtracting $\int f\,d\mu_2 + \int f\,d\varphi_2$ from both sides, we get the desired result. ■

In view of the above theorem, the most efficient way of extending the theory of integration and differentiation we have developed so far to any $\varphi \in \mathbf{LS}$ is through $\text{var}^+ \varphi$ and $\text{var}^- \varphi$. This explains our definition of integral with respect to φ given above. For example, if $\varphi = (2\boldsymbol{\lambda}_1 - \boldsymbol{\lambda}_1)/\mathfrak{A}_0$, then $\text{var}^+ \varphi = \boldsymbol{\lambda}_1$, $\text{var}^- \varphi = 0$, and $\int f\, d\varphi = \int f\, d\boldsymbol{\lambda}_1$ so that $\int f\, d\varphi$ exists in many cases where $2 \int f\, d\boldsymbol{\lambda}_1 - \int f\, d\boldsymbol{\lambda}_1$ does not.

We conclude by pointing out the vector-space properties of **LS**.

2.3. Theorem. **LS** is a vector space and if, for any $A \in \mathfrak{A}_0$ and $\varphi \in \mathbf{LS}$, $P_A(\varphi) = \text{var}\, \varphi(A)$, then P_A is a pseudonorm on **LS** and its restriction to $\{\varphi \in \mathbf{LS}\colon \varphi(\alpha \sim A) = 0 \text{ for every } \alpha \in \mathfrak{A}_0\}$ is a norm.

■ **proof:** This follows immediately from the facts that if $\varphi = \mu + \nu$, then $\text{var}^+ \varphi \leq \text{var}^+ \mu + \text{var}^+ \nu$, and that $\text{var}\, \varphi(A) = 0$ iff $\varphi(\alpha) = 0$ for every $\alpha \in \mathfrak{A}_0$, $\alpha \subset A$. ■

2.4. Exercises

1. Check that $\mathfrak{A}_0$ consists of bounded sets.
2. Let $V = \{\varphi \in \mathbf{LS}\colon \text{var}\, \varphi(\mathscr{R} \sim [0; 1]) = 0\}$ and, for $\varphi \in V$, let $P(\varphi) = \text{var}\, \varphi([0; 1])$. Check that P is a complete norm on V and that, for any sequence φ in V and $\psi \in V$ we have

$$\psi = \lim_n \varphi_n \text{ in } P \text{ iff } \psi(A) = \lim_n \varphi_n(A) \text{ for every } A \in \mathfrak{A}_0$$

(*Hint:* use the Hahn decomposition theorem.)

3. For every $n \in \boldsymbol{\omega}$ and $\mu, \nu \in \mathbf{LS}$, let $d_n(\mu, \nu) = \text{var}\, (\mu - \nu)([-n; n])$ and

$$\rho = \sum_{n \in \omega} \frac{1}{2^n} \frac{d_n}{1 + d_n}.$$

Check that ρ is a complete metric on **LS** and that, for any sequence φ in **LS** and $\psi \in \mathbf{LS}$, we have $\psi = \lim_n \varphi_n$ in ρ iff $\psi(A) = \lim_n \varphi_n(A)$ for every $A \in \mathfrak{A}_0$. The topology induced by ρ is called the strong or norm topology on **LS**.

4. If $\varphi \in \mathbf{LS}$ and $\varphi([a; b]) = 0$ for every $a, b \in \mathscr{R}$, then $\varphi(A) = 0$ for every $A \in \mathfrak{A}_0$.

3. FUNCTIONS OF BOUNDED VARIATION

In view of the connection between Lebesgue-Stieltjes measures and nondecreasing functions on the line, we have seen how the theory of integration and differentiation which we have developed applies immediately to nondecreasing functions. It is a simple matter to extend the theory to differences of such functions. In this section we characterize those functions which can be expressed as the difference of nondecreasing functions and relate them to signed Lebesgue-Stieltjes measures. Historically, the concepts of variation and absolute continuity for measures which we introduced in previous chapters are based on the corresponding concepts for functions which we give in the definitions below.

3.1. Definitions
For $-\infty < a < b < \infty$ and any function f with $[a; b] \subset \text{domain} f$ and $f[[a; b]] \subset \mathscr{R}$:

(1) $\mathbf{V}(f; a, b) = \sup \{\Sigma_{i=0}^{n} |f(x_{i+1}) - f(x_i)|;\ n \in \boldsymbol{\omega}$ and
$$a \le x_i \le x_{i+1} \le b \quad \text{for} \quad i = 0, \cdots, n\}.$$

(2) f is absolutely continuous on $[a; b]$ iff, for every $\epsilon > 0$, there exists $\delta > 0$ such that if $n \in \boldsymbol{\omega}$, $a \le x_i \le y_i \le x_{i+1} \le b$ for $i = 0, \cdots, n$ and $\Sigma_{i=0}^{n} (y_i - x_i) < \delta$, then $\Sigma_{i=0}^{n} |f(y_i) - f(x_i)| < \epsilon$.

(3) $\mathbf{D}f(x) = \lim_{h \to 0} (f(x+h) - f(x))/h$.

(4) f is singular iff $\mathbf{D}f(x) = 0$ for $\boldsymbol{\lambda}_1$-a.a. $x \in \mathscr{R}$.

(5) $$\int_a^b f(x)\,dx = \int_{[a;b]} f\,d\boldsymbol{\lambda}_1,$$
$$\int_b^a f(x)\,dx = -\int_a^b f(x)\,dx.$$

(6) $\mathbf{BV} = \{f{:}f$ is on $\mathscr{R}$ to $\mathscr{R}$ and $\mathbf{V}(f; a, b) < \infty$ whenever $-\infty < a \le b < \infty\}$.

(7) $\mathbf{AC} = \{f{:}f$ is on $\mathscr{R}$ to $\mathscr{R}$ and f is absolutely continuous on $[a; b]$ whenever $-\infty < a \le b < \infty\}$.

As an immediate consequence of the definitions, we have the following lemma whose proof is left as an exercise.

3.2. Lemma. Let f, g be on $\mathscr{R}$ to $\mathscr{R}$ and $-\infty < a \le b \le c < \infty$. Then

(1) $0 \le \mathbf{V}(f; a, c) = \mathbf{V}(f; a, b) + \mathbf{V}(f; b, c) \le \infty$.

(2) $\mathbf{V}(f+g; a, b) \le \mathbf{V}(f; a, b) + \mathbf{V}(g; a, b)$.

(3) f is nondecreasing iff $\mathbf{V}(f; a, b) = f(b) - f(a)$.

We now state some of the main properties of functions in **BV** and **AC**.

3.3. Theorems

(1) $\mathbf{AC} \subset \mathbf{BV}$.

(2) $f \in \mathbf{BV}$ iff there exist nondecreasing functions f_1 and f_2 such that $f = f_1 - f_2$.

(3) $f \in \mathbf{AC}$ iff there exist nondecreasing functions $f_1, f_2 \in \mathbf{AC}$ such that $f = f_1 - f_2$.

■ **proofs**

(1) Let $f \in \mathbf{AC}$ and $-\infty < a < b < \infty$. Then there exists $\delta > 0$ such that if $a \le x \le y \le b$ and $y - x < \delta$ then $\mathbf{V}(f; x, y) < 1$. Choose $n \in \boldsymbol{\omega}$

and x_i so that $a = x_0$, $x_i < x_{i+1}$, $b = x_{n+1}$ and $x_{i+1} - x_i < \delta$ for $i = 0, \cdots, n$. Then, by 3.2.1, $\mathbf{V}(f; a, b) = \Sigma_{i=0}^{n} \mathbf{V}(f; x_i, x_{i+1}) < n + 1 < \infty$.

(2) Let $f \in \mathbf{BV}$,

$$f_1(x) = \begin{cases} \mathbf{V}(f; 0, x) & \text{if} \quad x \geq 0 \\ -\mathbf{V}(f; x, 0) & \text{if} \quad x < 0 \end{cases}$$

and $f_2 = f_1 - f$. Then clearly $f = f_1 - f_2$ and, by 3.2.1, f_1 is nondecreasing and, for $-\infty < x < y < \infty$,

$$\begin{aligned} f_2(y) - f_2(x) = f_1(y) - f(y) - f_1(x) + f(x) &= \mathbf{V}(f; x, y) - f(y) + f(x) \\ \geq \mathbf{V}(f; x, y) - |f(y) - f(x)| &\geq 0, \end{aligned}$$

so that f_2 is also nondecreasing. The converse follows from 3.2.2 and 3.2.3.

(3) Let $f \in \mathbf{AC}$ and f_1, f_2 as in (2) above. To see that $f_1 \in \mathbf{AC}$, let $-\infty < a < b < \infty$ and $\epsilon > 0$. Then there exists $\delta > 0$ such that if $n \in \boldsymbol{\omega}$, $a \leq x_i \leq y_i < x_{i+1} \leq b$ for $i = 0, \cdots, n$ and $\Sigma_{i=0}^{n} (y_i - x_i) < \delta$, then $\Sigma_{i=0}^{n} |f(y_i) - f(x_i)| < \epsilon$ and hence also $\Sigma_{i=0}^{n} \mathbf{V}(f; x_i, y_i) < \epsilon$, since any subdivision which refines each $[x_i; y_i]$ will still have total length less than δ. Thus $f_1 \in \mathbf{AC}$ and hence $f_2 \in \mathbf{AC}$. ■

3.4. Theorems

(1) If $f \in \mathbf{BV}$, then $\mathbf{D}f(x) \in \mathscr{R}$ for $\boldsymbol{\lambda}_1$-a.a. $x \in \mathscr{R}$, $\mathbf{D}f(x)$ is $\boldsymbol{\lambda}_1$-measurable in x and, for $-\infty < a \leq b < \infty$,

$$\int_a^b |\mathbf{D}f(x)| \, dx \leq \mathbf{V}(f; a, b) < \infty.$$

(2) If $f \in \mathbf{AC}$, then for $-\infty < a \leq b < \infty$,

$$\int_a^b \mathbf{D}f(x) \, dx = f(b) - f(a)$$

and

$$\int_a^b |\mathbf{D}f(x)| \, dx = V(f; a, b).$$

(3) If $g \in \mathbf{MF}_{\boldsymbol{\lambda}_1}$ and, for every $x \in \mathscr{R}$, $f(x) = \int_0^x g(t) \, dt \in \mathscr{R}$, then $f \in \mathbf{AC}$ and $\mathbf{D}f(x) = g(x)$ for $\boldsymbol{\lambda}_1$-a.a. $x \in \mathscr{R}$.

(4) Let $f \in \mathbf{BV}$, $f_1(x) = \int_0^x \mathbf{D}f(t) \, dt$ for $x \in \mathscr{R}$ and $f_2 = f - f_1$. Then $f_1 \in \mathbf{AC}$, f_2 is singular and $f = f_1 + f_2$. Moreover, if $g_1 \in \mathbf{AC}$, g_2 is singular and $f = g_1 + g_2$, then $g_1(x) - f_1(x)$ and $g_2(x) - f_2(x)$ are constant for $\boldsymbol{\lambda}_1$-a.a. $x \in \mathscr{R}$.

■ **proofs**

(1) Let $f = f_1 - f_2$, where f_1 and f_2 are nondecreasing functions. By 4.2 and 4.3.1, Chapter 8, $\mathbf{D}f_1(x)$ and $\mathbf{D}f_2(x)$ are finite for $\boldsymbol{\lambda}_1$-a.a. $x \in \mathscr{R}$

and are $\boldsymbol{\lambda}_1$-measurable in x. Hence $\mathbf{D}f(x) \in \mathscr{R}$ for $\boldsymbol{\lambda}_1$-a.a. $x \in \mathscr{R}$ and is $\boldsymbol{\lambda}_1$-measurable in x. Let $-\infty < a < b < \infty$ and $g(x) = \mathbf{V}(f; a, x)$. Since, for $x < y$ we have

$$g(y) - g(x) = \mathbf{V}(f; x, y) \geq |f(y) - f(x)|,$$

we see that, $|\mathbf{D}f(x)| \leq \mathbf{D}g(x)$ for $\boldsymbol{\lambda}_1$-a.a. $x \in (a; b)$ and hence, by 4.2 and 4.3.1, Chapter 8,

$$\int_a^b |\mathbf{D}f(x)|\, dx \leq \int_a^b \mathbf{D}g(x)\, dx \leq g(b) - g(a)$$
$$= \mathbf{V}(f; a, b).$$

(2) Let $f = f_1 - f_2$ where f_1 and f_2 are nondecreasing functions and f_1, $f_2 \in \mathbf{AC}$ and let $-\infty < a < b < \infty$. Then, applying 4.3.1e, Chapter 8, to f_1 and f_2, we get $\int_a^b \mathbf{D}f(x) = f(b) - f(a)$. Moreover, if $n \in \boldsymbol{\omega}$ and $a \leq x_i \leq x_{i+1} \leq b$ for $i = 0, \cdots, n$, then

$$\sum_{i=0}^{n} |f(x_{i+1}) - f(x_i)| = \sum_{i=0}^{n} \left| \int_{x_i}^{x_{i+1}} \mathbf{D}f(t)\, dt \right|$$
$$\leq \sum_{i=0}^{n} \int_{x_i}^{x_{i+1}} |\mathbf{D}f(t)|\, dt$$
$$\leq \int_a^b |\mathbf{D}f(t)|\, dt.$$

Thus, $\mathbf{V}(f; a, b) \leq \int_a^b |\mathbf{D}f(t)|\, dt$ and hence, by (1), equality holds.

(3) Let $g \in \mathbf{MF}_{\boldsymbol{\lambda}_1}$ and $f(x) = \int_0^x g(t)\, dt \in \mathscr{R}$ for $x \in \mathscr{R}$. To see that $f \in \mathbf{AC}$, let $-\infty < a \leq b < \infty$ and $\epsilon > 0$. Since $\int_a^b |g(t)|\, dt < \infty$, choose $K > 0$ so that if $A = \{t \in [a; b]\colon\ |g(t)| > K\}$, then $\int_A |g(t)|\, dt < \epsilon/2$ and let $\delta = \epsilon/2K$. If $n \in \boldsymbol{\omega}$, $a \leq x_i \leq y_i \leq x_{i+1} \leq b$ for $i = 0, \cdots, n$ and $\Sigma_{i=0}^n (y_i - x_i) < \delta$, then

$$\sum_{i=0}^{n} |f(y_i) - f(x_i)| \leq \sum_{i=0}^{n} \int_{x_i}^{y_i} |g(t)|\, dt$$
$$\leq \int_A |g(t)|\, dt + \sum_{i=0}^{n} \int_{x_i}^{y_i} K\, dt$$
$$\leq \frac{\epsilon}{2} + K \cdot \delta = \epsilon.$$

To see that $\mathbf{D}f(x) = g(x)$ for $\boldsymbol{\lambda}_1$-a.a. $x \in \mathscr{R}$, let $h(x) = \mathbf{D}f(x) - g(x)$. By (2), we have $\int_a^b h(x)\, dx = 0$ for any $a, b \in \mathscr{R}$, hence $\int_A h(x)\, dx = 0$ for any open A and therefore also for any $A \in \mathscr{M}_{\boldsymbol{\lambda}_1}$. Thus, $\int h^+\, d\boldsymbol{\lambda}_1 = 0 = \int h^-\, d\boldsymbol{\lambda}_1$ so that $h(x) = 0$ for $\boldsymbol{\lambda}_1$-*a.a.* $x \in \mathscr{R}$.

(4) This follows immediately from (3). ∎

We now indicate the connection between **BV** and **LS**.

3.5. Theorem. There exists a unique linear function μ on **BV** onto **LS** such that: if $f \in \mathbf{BV}$, $\bar{f}(x) = \lim_{t\to x^+} f(t)$ and $\underline{f}(x) = \lim_{t\to x^-} f(t)$ for $x \in \mathscr{R}$ and $-\infty < a \leq b < \infty$, then

(1) $\mu_f([a; b]) = \bar{f}(b) - \underline{f}(a)$.

(2) $\mu_f = \mu_{\bar{f}} = \mu_{\underline{f}}$

(3) $\mu_f(A) = 0$ for all $A \in \mathfrak{A}_0$ iff $\bar{f}(x) = \underline{f}(x) =$ constant for all $x \in \mathscr{R}$.

(4) $\mu_f \in \mathbf{LS}_+$ iff $\bar{f}$ is nondecreasing iff $\underline{f}$ is nondecreasing.

(5) var $\mu_f(\{a\}) = 0$ iff $\mu_f(\{a\}) = 0$ iff $\bar{f}(a) = \underline{f}(a)$.

(6) var μ_f is absolutely continuous with respect to $\boldsymbol{\lambda}_1$ iff $\bar{f} = \underline{f} \in \mathbf{AC}$.

(7) var μ_f is singular with respect to $\boldsymbol{\lambda}_1$ iff $\bar{f}$ is singular iff $\underline{f}$ is singular.

(8) var $\mu_f((a; b]) = \mathbf{V}(\bar{f}; a, b)$ and var $\mu_f([a; b)) = \mathbf{V}(\underline{f}; a, b)$.

■ **proof:** For any $f \in \mathbf{BV}$, choose nondecreasing functions f_1, f_2 such that $f = f_1 - f_2$, let μ_1, μ_2 be the Lebesgue-Stieltjes outer measures generated by f_1, f_2, respectively, and $\mu_f = (\mu_1 - \mu_2)/\mathfrak{A}_0$. Then, by 2.2, Chapter 6, and exercise 2.4.4, Chapter 9, we see that (1) and (2) hold, μ_f is independent of the choice of f_1, f_2, and that μ is a linear function on **BV** onto **LS**. Clearly there is a unique such function. Let $\varphi_1 = \text{var}^+ \mu_f$ and $\varphi_2 = \text{var}^- \mu_f$.

(3) By 2.4.4, $\mu_f(A) = 0$ for all $A \in \mathfrak{A}_0$ iff, for all $x, y \in \mathscr{R}$, $\mu_f([x; y]) = 0$, that is, $\bar{f}(x) = \underline{f}(x) =$ constant.

(4), (5) These follow from (1) after computing $\mu_f([a; b))$ and $\mu_f((a; b])$.

(6) If $f \in \mathbf{AC}$, then we may choose $f_1, f_2 \in \mathbf{AC}$ so that, by exercise 4.3.1, Chapter 8, μ_1 and μ_2 are absolutely continuous with respect to $\boldsymbol{\lambda}_1$ and since, by 2.2, $\varphi_1 \leq \mu_1$ and $\varphi_2 \leq \mu_2$ we see that var $\mu_f = \varphi_1 + \varphi_2$ is absolutely continuous with respect to $\boldsymbol{\lambda}_1$. If var μ_f is absolutely continuous with respect to $\boldsymbol{\lambda}_1$, let g_1, g_2 be the nondecreasing functions generating φ_1, φ_2. Then $g_1, g_2 \in \mathbf{AC}$ and $\bar{f} = \underline{f} = g_1 - g_2 + \text{constant} \in \mathbf{AC}$.

(7) Let $\mu_1 = \mu_1' + \mu_1''$ and $\mu_2 = \mu_2' + \mu_2''$, where μ_1', μ_2' are absolutely continuous with respect to $\boldsymbol{\lambda}_1$ and μ_1'', μ_2'' are singular with respect to $\boldsymbol{\lambda}_1$. If f is singular then $\mathbf{D}f_1(x) = \mathbf{D}f_2(x)$ for $\boldsymbol{\lambda}_1$-a.a. $x \in \mathscr{R}$ so that, by 4.2, 4.3.1, Chapter 8, $\mu_1' = \mu_2'$ and hence $\mu_f = \mu_1'' - \mu_2''$. Since $\varphi_1 \leq \mu_1''$ and $\varphi_2 \leq \mu_2''$, we conclude var $\mu_f = \varphi_1 + \varphi_2$ is singular with respect to $\boldsymbol{\lambda}_1$. For the converse, consider nondecreasing g_1, g_2 which generate φ_1, φ_2 and note that $\bar{f} = \bar{g}_1 - \bar{g}_2 + \text{constant}$ and $\underline{f} = \underline{g}_1 - \underline{g}_2 + \text{constant}$. Thus, if var μ_f is singular with respect to $\boldsymbol{\lambda}_1$, then, by 4.3.1, Chapter 8, g_1 and g_2 hence $\bar{f}$ and $\underline{f}$ are singular.

(8) Let $n \in \boldsymbol{\omega}$ and $a \leq x_i \leq x_{i+1} \leq b$ for $i = 0, \cdots, n$. Then, from (1),

$$\begin{aligned}\sum_{i=0}^{n} |\bar{f}(x_{i+1}) - \bar{f}(x_i)| &= \sum_{i=0}^{n} |\mu_f((x_i, x_{i+1}])| \\ &\leq \sum_{i=0}^{n} (\varphi_1 + \varphi_2)((x_i, x_{i+1}]) \\ &\leq (\varphi_1 + \varphi_2)((a; b]) = \text{var}\, \mu_f((a; b]).\end{aligned}$$

Thus, $\mathbf{V}(\bar{f}; a, b) \leq \operatorname{var} \mu_f((a; b])$. To reverse the inequality, by the Hahn decomposition theorem 2.1, Chapter 8, let $P \in \mathfrak{A}_0$ be such that $\varphi_1(A) = \mu_f(A \cap P)$ and $\varphi_2(A) = -\mu_f(A \sim P)$ for every $A \in \mathfrak{A}_0$, $A \subset (a; b]$. Given $\epsilon > 0$, choose compact C_1, C_2 so that $C_1 \subset P \cap (a; b]$, $C_2 \subset (a; b] \sim P$, $\varphi_1((a; b]) \leq \varphi_1(C_1) + \epsilon$ and $\varphi_2((a; b]) \leq \varphi_2(C_2) + \epsilon$. Let A, B be open in $(a; b]$, $C_1 \subset A$, $C_2 \subset B$, and $A \cap B = \phi$, then choose $n \in \boldsymbol{\omega}$ and mutually disjoint intervals $(x_i, y_i]$ and $(s_i; t_i]$ for $i = 0, \cdots, n$ such that

$$C_1 \subset \bigcup_{i=0}^{n} (x_i; y_i] = \alpha \subset A \quad \text{and} \quad C_2 \subset \bigcup_{i=0}^{n} (s_i; t_i] = \beta \subset B.$$

Then

$$\begin{aligned}
\operatorname{var} \mu_f((a; b]) &\leq \varphi_1(C_1) + \varphi_2(C_2) + 2\epsilon \leq \varphi_1(\alpha) + \varphi_2(\beta) + 2\epsilon \\
&= \mu_f(\alpha \cap P) - \mu_f(\beta \sim P) + 2\epsilon \\
&= \mu_f(\alpha) + \varphi_2(\alpha) - \mu_f(\beta) + \varphi_1(\beta) + 2\epsilon \\
&\leq \mu_f(\alpha) - \mu_f(\beta) + 4\epsilon \\
&= \sum_{i=0}^{n} (\bar{f}(y_i) - \bar{f}(x_i) + \bar{f}(t_i) - \bar{f}(s_i)) \\
&\leq \mathbf{V}(\bar{f}; a, b).
\end{aligned}$$

Thus, $\operatorname{var} \mu_f((a; b]) = \mathbf{V}(\bar{f}; a, b)$. Similarly, $\operatorname{var} \mu_f([a; b)) = \mathbf{V}(\underline{f}; a, b)$. ∎

3.6. Exercises

1. Prove lemma 3.2.
2. Let ρ be a metric on S, $-\infty < a < b < \infty$, f be a function on $[a; b]$ to S and

$$V = \sup\left\{\sum_{i=0}^{n} \rho(f(x_i), f(x_{i+1})); n \in \boldsymbol{\omega} \text{ and } a \leq x_i \leq x_{i+1} \leq b \text{ for } i = 0, \cdots, n\right\}.$$

Check that:

(a) $V = \sup \{\Sigma_{i=0}^{n} \operatorname{diam} f[[x_i; x_{i+1}]]; n \in \boldsymbol{\omega}$ and $a \leq x_i \leq x_{i+1} \leq b$ for $i = 0, \cdots, n\}$.

(b) If f is continuous and one to one, then $V = \lim_{\delta \to 0^+} \inf \{\Sigma_{i\in\omega} \operatorname{diam} \alpha_i; \alpha$ is a sequence with $\alpha_i \subset S$ and $\operatorname{diam} \alpha_i < \delta$ for $i \in \boldsymbol{\omega}$ and range $f \subset \bigcup_{i\in\omega} \alpha_i\}$.

(The expression above is called the linear measure or Hausdorff one-dimensional measure of range f. Thus, V extends the notion of variation to functions having range in a metric space. Since V represents the length of the curve f, we see that linear measure extends the notion of length to sets which are not curves.)

4. LINEAR FUNCTIONALS ON $\mathbf{C}_0$

We have seen that a measure gives rise through the integral to a linear functional on a family of functions. We shall now consider the family of continuous functions on the line vanishing outside a compact set and characterize certain linear functionals on this family in terms of signed Lebesgue-Stieltjes measures. Although we restrict ourselves to the real line, the ideas we introduce here extend without much effort to more general topological spaces.

4.1. Definitions. For $A \subset \mathcal{R}$:

(1) $\mathbf{C}_0(A) = \{f: f$ is a continuous function on $\mathcal{R}$ to $\mathcal{R}$ and there exists a compact $K \subset A$ such that $f(x) = 0$ for $x \in \mathcal{R} \sim K\}$.

(2) $\mathbf{C}_0^+(A) = \{f \in \mathbf{C}_0(A): f(x) \geq 0$ for $x \in \mathcal{R}\}$.

(3) For $f \in \mathbf{C}_0(\mathcal{R})$:
$\|f\|_\infty = \sup \{|f(x)|; x \in \mathcal{R}\}$.

(4) $\mathbf{C}_0^* = \{l: l$ is a linear function on $\mathbf{C}_0(\mathcal{R})$ to $\mathcal{R}$ and for every compact $K \subset \mathcal{R}$ there exists $M < \infty$ such that, for every $f \in \mathbf{C}_0(K)$, $|l(f)| \leq M \cdot \|f\|_\infty\}$.

(5) $\mathbf{C}_0^{*+} = \{l \in \mathbf{C}_0^*: l(f) \geq 0$ for $f \in \mathbf{C}_0^+(\mathcal{R})\}$.

(6) For $l \in \mathbf{C}_0^*$:

$$\|l\|_A = \inf \{M: M \geq 0 \text{ and } |l(f)| \leq M \cdot \|f\|_\infty \text{ for every } f \in \mathbf{C}_0(A)\}.$$

We should observe that the elements of $\mathbf{C}_0^*$ are not necessarily continuous linear functionals on $\mathbf{C}_0(\mathcal{R})$ in the topology induced by the sup norm on $\mathbf{C}_0(\mathcal{R})$. We do not restrict ourselves to the continuous ones because, as we shall see, these correspond to the bounded measures. The essential part of the Riesz representation theorem 4.5 is theorem 4.4 below. We first give lemmas 4.2 and 4.3 primarily to indicate key properties of the real line used in the proof of 4.4 which are also possessed by many other topological spaces (for example, locally compact and regular).

4.2. Lemma. Let A be compact, B be open and $A \subset B \subset \mathcal{R}$. Then there exists $f \in \mathbf{C}_0(\mathcal{R})$ such that $\mathbf{1}_A \leq f \leq \mathbf{1}_B$.

■ **proof:** Choose $n \in \boldsymbol{\omega}$ and disjoint bounded open intervals $(x_i; y_i)$ for $i = 0, \cdots, n$ such that $A \subset \bigcup_{i=0}^n (x_i; y_i) \subset B$. Let $a_i = \inf (A \cap (x_i; y_i))$ and $b_i = \sup (A \cap (x_i; y_i))$. Then $A \cap (x_i; y_i) \subset [a_i; b_i] \subset (x_i; y_i)$ and there exists a continuous (in fact, piecewise linear) function g_i such that $\mathbf{1}_{[a_i;b_i]} \leq g_i \leq \mathbf{1}_{(x_i;y_i)}$. Let $f = \Sigma_{i=0}^n g_i$. ■

4.3. Lemma. If A and B are open, C is compact and $C \subset A \cup B \subset \mathcal{R}$, then there exist compact α, β such that $\alpha \subset A$, $\beta \subset B$ and $C = \alpha \cup \beta$.

■ **proof:** Let $C' = C \sim B$, A' be an open set with $C' \subset A' \subset$ closure $A' \subset A$, $\alpha = C \cap$ closure A' and $\beta = C \sim A'$. ■

4.4. Theorem. For every $l \in \mathbf{C}_0^{*+}$ there exists a unique Lebesgue-Stieltjes outer measure μ such that

(1) $l(f) = \int f\,d\mu$ for every $f \in \mathbf{C}_0(\mathscr{R})$

(2) $\|l\|_A = \mu(A)$ for every open $A \subset \mathscr{R}$.

■ **proof:** Given $l \in \mathbf{C}_0^{*+}$, let

$$\tau(A) = \inf \{l(f); f \in \mathbf{C}_0(\mathscr{R}) \text{ and } \mathbf{1}_A \leq f\},$$

$$\tau'(A) = \sup \{\tau(\alpha); \alpha \text{ compact and } \alpha \subset A\},$$

and μ be the Carathéodory measure on $\mathscr{R}$ generated by τ' and the family of open sets. We first check properties of τ, τ'.

(a) If A and B are compact then $\tau(A \cup B) \leq \tau(A) + \tau(B)$ and if in addition $A \cap B = \phi$, then $\tau(A \cup B) = \tau(A) + \tau(B)$.
Indeed, if $f, g \in \mathbf{C}_0(\mathscr{R})$ and $\mathbf{1}_A \leq f$, $\mathbf{1}_B \leq g$, then $f + g \in \mathbf{C}_0(\mathscr{R})$ and $\mathbf{1}_{A \cup B} \leq \mathbf{1}_A + \mathbf{1}_B \leq f + g$ so that $\tau(A \cup B) \leq l(f) + l(g)$. Taking the inf over f and g, we get $\tau(A \cup B) \leq \tau(A) + \tau(B)$. If A and B are compact and $A \cap B = \phi$, let A', B' be open, disjoint sets with $A \subset A'$ and $B \subset B'$ and by lemma 4.2, choose $f, g \in \mathbf{C}_0(\mathscr{R})$ such that $\mathbf{1}_A \leq f \leq \mathbf{1}_{A'}$ and $\mathbf{1}_B \leq g \leq \mathbf{1}_{B'}$. Then for any $h \in \mathbf{C}_0(\mathscr{R})$ with $\mathbf{1}_{A \cup B} \leq h$, we have $\mathbf{1}_A \leq h \cdot f$, $\mathbf{1}_B \leq h \cdot g$ and $h \cdot f + h \cdot g \leq h$ so that:

$$\tau(A) + \tau(B) \leq l(h \cdot f) + l(h \cdot g) = l(h \cdot f + h \cdot g) \leq l(h).$$

Taking the inf over h, we get $\tau(A) + \tau(B) \leq \tau(A \cup B)$.

(b) If A is a sequence of open sets, then

$$\tau'\left(\bigcup_{n \in \omega} A_n\right) \leq \sum_{n \in \omega} \tau'(A_n).$$

Indeed if C is compact and $C \subset \bigcup_{n \in \omega} A_n$, then, for some $N \in \boldsymbol{\omega}$, $C \subset \bigcup_{n=0}^N A_n$. By lemma 4.3 and induction there exist compact $\alpha_n \subset A_n$ such that $C = \bigcup_{n=0}^N \alpha_n$. Then by (a):

$$\tau(C) \leq \sum_{n=0}^{N} \tau(\alpha_n) \leq \sum_{n \in \omega} \tau'(A_n).$$

We now check properties of μ.

(c) If A is open, then $A \in \mathscr{M}_\mu$.
Indeed, given $T \subset \mathscr{R}$ with $\mu(T) < \infty$ and $\epsilon > 0$, let T' be open, $T \subset T'$ and $\tau'(T') < \mu(T) + \epsilon$. Then choose compact α, β such that $\alpha \subset (T' \cap A)$ and $\tau'(T' \cap A) < \tau(\alpha) + \epsilon$, $\beta \subset (T' \sim \alpha)$ and $\tau'(T' \sim \alpha) < \tau(\beta) + \epsilon$. Then, by (a) we have

$$\begin{aligned} &\mu(T \cap A) + \mu(T \sim A) \\ &\qquad \leq \tau'(T' \cap A) + \tau'(T' \sim \alpha) < \tau(\alpha) + \tau(\beta) + 2\epsilon \\ &\qquad = \tau(\alpha \cup \beta) + 2\epsilon \leq \tau'(T') + 2\epsilon < \mu(T) + 3\epsilon. \end{aligned}$$

(d) For any $A \subset \mathscr{R}$, $\mu(A) = \inf\{\mu(\alpha);\ \alpha \text{ is open and } A \subset \alpha\}$,
$= \inf\{\tau'(\alpha);\ \alpha \text{ is open and } A \subset \alpha\}$.

This follows immediately from the fact that, by (b), for any open α, $\mu(\alpha) = \tau'(\alpha)$.

(e) For any compact A, $\tau(A) \leq \mu(A) < \infty$.
Indeed, if B is open, closure B is compact and $A \subset B$, then $\tau(A) \leq \tau'(B) \leq \tau$ (closure B) $< \infty$, hence $\tau(A) \leq \mu(A) < \infty$. (Actually, $\mu(A) = \tau(A)$. See exercise 4.6.1.)

Thus, by 2.3, Chapter 6, we see that μ is a Lebesgue-Stieltjes outer measure.

(f) If $f \in \mathbf{C}_0(\mathscr{R})$ then $l(f) = \int f\,d\mu$. We may suppose $f \geq 0$ and let K be compact and $f(x) = 0$ for $x \in \mathscr{R} \sim K$. Since $\mu(\{x : f(x) > 0\}) < \infty$, there are only a countable number of positive t with $\mu(f^{-1}[\{t\}]) > 0$. Given $\epsilon > 0$, choose $n \in \boldsymbol{\omega}$ and $0 = t_0 \leq t_i \leq t_{i+1} \leq t_{n+1} = \|f\|_\infty$ for $i = 0, \cdots, n$ so that $\mu(f^{-1}[\{t_i\}]) = 0$ and if $A_i = f^{-1}[(t_i, t_{i+1})]$, $B_i = f^{-1}[[t_i; t_{i+1}]] \cap K$, then

$$\sum_{i=0}^{n} t_{i+1} \cdot \mu(B_i) - \epsilon < \int f\,d\mu < \sum_{i=0}^{n} t_i \cdot \mu(A_i) + \epsilon.$$

Suppose $\|f\|_\infty > 0$ and let $\delta = \epsilon/((n+1)\cdot\|f\|_\infty)$. Since A_i is open, let α_i be compact, $\alpha_i \subset A_i$, $\mu(A_i) < \tau(\alpha_i) + \delta$ and, by lemma 4.2, let $g_i \in \mathbf{C}_0(\mathscr{R})$ and $\mathbf{1}_{\alpha_i} \leq g_i \leq \mathbf{1}_{A_i}$. Then $\tau(\alpha_i) \leq l(g_i)$ and $\mu(A_i) < l(g_i) + \delta$. Next, since B_i is compact, choose $h_i \in \mathbf{C}_0(\mathscr{R})$ so that $\mathbf{1}_{B_i} \leq h_i$ and $l(h_i) < \tau(B_i) + \delta \leq \mu(B_i) + \delta$. Then:

$$0 \leq \sum_{i=0}^{n} t_i g_i \leq f \leq \sum_{i=0}^{n} t_{i+1} h_i;$$

hence, since $l \in \mathbf{C}_0^{*+}$,

$$\sum_{i=0}^{n} t_i l(g_i) \leq l(f) \leq \sum_{i=0}^{n} t_{i+1} l(h_i),$$

$$\sum_{i=0}^{n} t_i \mu(A_i) - \epsilon \leq l(f) \leq \sum_{i=0}^{n} t_{i+1} \mu(B_i) + \epsilon,$$

$$\int f\,d\mu - 2\epsilon < l(f) < \int f\,d\mu + 2\epsilon.$$

(g) If ν is a Lebesgue-Stieltjes outer measure with $\int f\,d\nu = \int f\,d\mu$ for every $f \in \mathbf{C}_0(\mathscr{R})$, then $\nu = \mu$.
It is enough to check that if A is compact, then $\nu(A) = \mu(A)$. Given $\epsilon > 0$, choose A' open such that $A \subset A'$ and $\mu(A') < \mu(A) + \epsilon$ and, by lemma 4.2, let $f \in \mathbf{C}_0(\mathscr{R})$, $\mathbf{1}_A \leq f \leq \mathbf{1}_{A'}$. Then $\nu(A) \leq \int f\,d\nu = \int f\,d\mu \leq \mu(A') < \mu(A) + \epsilon$. Thus $\nu(A) \leq \mu(A)$ and similarly $\mu(A) \leq \nu(A)$.

(h) If A is open, then $\|l\|_A = \mu(A)$.
For any $f \in \mathbf{C}_0(A)$, we have

$$|l(f)| \leq \int |f| \, d\mu \leq \mu(A) \cdot \|f\|_\infty.$$

Hence $\|l\|_A \leq \mu(A)$. On the other hand, for any compact $\alpha \subset A$, there exists, by lemma 4.2, $f \in \mathbf{C}_0(A)$ with $\mathbf{1}_\alpha \leq f \leq \mathbf{1}_A$ so that, $l(f) \geq \tau(\alpha) = \tau(\alpha) \cdot \|f\|_\infty$. Thus $\tau(\alpha) \leq \|l\|_A$ and therefore

$$\mu(A) = \tau'(A) = \sup \{\tau(\alpha); \ \alpha \text{ compact and } \alpha \subset A\} \leq \|l\|_A. \ \blacksquare$$

We are now in a position to give the fundamental theorem of this section.

4.5. Theorem (Riesz representation). There exists a unique linear function μ on $\mathbf{C}_0^*$ onto $\mathbf{LS}$ such that if $l \in \mathbf{C}_0^*$ then:
(1) $\int f \, d\mu_l = l(f)$ for every $f \in \mathbf{C}_0(\mathscr{R})$.
(2) $\mu_l \in \mathbf{LS}_+$ iff $l \in \mathbf{C}_0^{*+}$.
(3) if A is open, then var $\mu_l(A) = \|l\|_A$.

■ **proof:** By exercise 4.3.3, Chapter 5, for every $l \in \mathbf{C}_0^*$, there exist $l', l'' \in \mathbf{C}_0^{*+}$ such that $l = l' - l''$ (for example, let $l'(f) = \sup \{l(g);\ g \in \mathbf{C}_0(\mathscr{R}) \text{ and } 0 \leq g \leq f\}$ for $f \in \mathbf{C}_0^+(\mathscr{R})$ and $l'' = l' - l$). Let μ_1, μ_2 be the Lebesgue-Stieltjes outer measures associated with l' and l'' by theorem 4.4, $\varphi = \mu_1 - \mu_2/\mathfrak{A}_0$ and $\mu_l = \varphi$. By 4.4, μ is a unique linear function on $\mathbf{C}_0^*$ onto $\mathbf{LS}$. Then (1) follows immediately from 4.4 and 2.2.6, whereas (2) is a consequence of (1). To check (3), let A be open, $\varphi_1 = \text{var}^+ \varphi$ and $\varphi_2 = \text{var}^- \varphi$. Then for any $f \in \mathbf{C}_0(A)$,

$$|l(f)| = \left| \int f \, d\varphi \right| \leq \int |f| \, d\varphi_1 + \int |f| \, d\varphi_2 \leq (\varphi_1 + \varphi_2)(A) \cdot \|f\|_\infty.$$

Thus, $\|l\|_A \leq \text{var}\, \varphi(A)$. To reverse the inequality, suppose A is bounded, apply the Hahn decomposition theorem 2.1, Chapter 7 to $\mathfrak{A} = \{\alpha \in \mathfrak{A}_0 : \alpha \subset A\}$ and get $P \in \mathfrak{A}$ such that, for every $\alpha \in \mathfrak{A}$, $\varphi_1(\alpha) = \varphi(\alpha \cap P)$ and $\varphi_2(\alpha) = -\varphi(\alpha \sim P)$. For any $\epsilon > 0$, choose compact α, β such that $\alpha \subset P$ and $\varphi_1(A) < \varphi_1(\alpha) + \epsilon$, $\beta \subset A \sim P$ and $\varphi_2(A) < \varphi_2(\beta) + \epsilon$. Then find disjoint, open α', β' such that $\alpha \subset \alpha' \subset A$, $\beta \subset \beta' \subset A$ and by lemma 4.2, choose $f, g \in \mathbf{C}_0(A)$ such that $\mathbf{1}_\alpha \leq f \leq \mathbf{1}_{\alpha'}$ and $\mathbf{1}_\beta \leq g \leq \mathbf{1}_{\beta'}$. Since, for any $B \subset A \sim (\alpha \cup \beta)$, $\varphi_1(B) < \epsilon$ and $\varphi_2(B) < \epsilon$ we have:

$$\begin{aligned} \varphi_1(\alpha) \leq \int f \, d\varphi_1 &= \int_P f \, d\varphi = \int f \, d\varphi - \int_{\alpha' \sim P} f \, d\varphi \\ &\leq \int f \, d\varphi + \varphi_2(\alpha' \sim P) < \int f \, d\varphi + \epsilon = l(f) + \epsilon \end{aligned}$$

and, similarly, $\varphi_2(\beta) \leq \int g\, d\varphi_2 < l(g) + \epsilon$. Hence:

$$\varphi_1(A) + \varphi_2(A) < \varphi_1(\alpha) + \varphi_2(\beta) + 2\epsilon < l(f) + l(g) + 4\epsilon$$
$$= l(f + g) + 4\epsilon \leq \|l\|_A + 4\epsilon.$$

Thus, var $\varphi(A) \leq \|l\|_A$. If A is unbounded, consider $A \cap (-n; n)$ for $n \in \boldsymbol{\omega}$ and pass to the limit. ■

The identification of $\mathbf{C}_0^*$ with **LS** given by the Riesz representation theorem above enables one to transfer concepts which are natural in one space to the other. For example, any $l \in \mathbf{C}_0^*$ can be extended to a linear functional on a much wider class than $\mathbf{C}_0(\mathscr{R})$, say $\{f: \int f\, d\mu \in \mathscr{R}$ for every $\mu \in \mathbf{LS}\}$, through $\int f\, d\mu_l$. Frequently, such transfers are carried out without any explicit passage from one space to the other. Thus, integration theory can be developed without explicit reference to a measure and the extension mentioned above can be carried out without appeal to the Riesz representation theorem. However, the ideas and techniques involved are essentially those developed here. The difference is more one of terminology and outlook.

4.6. Exercises

1. If l, μ are as in theorem 4.4, check that for any compact A, $\mu(A) = \inf\{l(f); f \in \mathbf{C}_0(\mathscr{R})$ and $\mathbf{1}_A \leq f\}$.
2. Let μ be the function given by the Riesz representation theorem 4.5 and $l \in \mathbf{C}_0^*$. If $l' \in \mathbf{C}_0^*$, for $f \in \mathbf{C}_0^+(\mathscr{R})$,

$$l'(f) = \sup\{l(g); g \in \mathbf{C}_0(\mathscr{R}) \quad \text{and} \quad 0 \leq g \leq f\}$$

and $l'' = l' - l$, then $\mu_{l'} = \text{var}^+ \mu_l$ and $\mu_{l''} = \text{var}^- \mu_l$.

3. Let $\mathbf{C}_\infty = \{f: f$ is continuous on $\mathscr{R}$ to $\mathscr{R}$ and $\lim_{\alpha\to\pm\infty} f(x) = 0\}$

$$\mathbf{C}_\infty^* = \{l: l \text{ is a linear functional on } C \text{ and there exists } M < \infty \text{ such that } |l(f)| \leq M \cdot \|f\|_\infty \text{ for every } f \in \mathbf{C}_\infty\}.$$

Show that:
(a) $l \in \mathbf{C}_\infty^*$ iff l is a linear functional on C_∞ and $l/\mathbf{C}_0(\mathscr{R}) \in \mathbf{C}_0^*$.
(b) identify (as in theorem 4.5) $\mathbf{C}_\infty^*$ with $\{\mu \in \mathbf{LS}$: var $\mu(\mathscr{R}) < \infty\}$.

4. Introduce a topology on $\mathbf{C}_0(\mathscr{R})$ so that $\mathbf{C}_0^*$ consists of all continuous linear functionals on $\mathbf{C}_0(\mathscr{R})$. Show that such a topology can be induced by a metric.

SYMBOLS

iff, 3
ϵ, $\notin$, 3
$\subset$, $\supset$, $=$, 3
$\emptyset$, 3
$\{x, y, \cdots, z\}$, 3
$\{x: P(x)\}$, 4
$\{x \in A: P(x)\}$, 4
$\{m, \cdots, n\}$, 4
$\mathscr{R}$, $\mathscr{R}_+$, 4
$[a; b]$, 4, 58, 79
$(a; b)$, 4, 58, 79
$(a; b]$, 4, 58
$[a; b)$, 4, 58
$\mathscr{R}\mathbf{a}$, $\mathscr{R}\mathbf{a}_+$, 4
$\boldsymbol{\omega}$, $\boldsymbol{\omega}_+$, 4
domain f, 4
range f, 4
$f[A]$, 4
$f|A$, 4
f^{-1}, 4
$f \circ g$, 4
$\mathbf{a}$, 5
$A \cup B$, 5
$\bigcup_{i=m}^{n} A_i$, 5
$\bigcup_{i \in I} A_i$, 5
$\bigcup F$, 5
$\{A_i; i \in I\}$, 5
$\{A_i; i \in I$ and $P(i)\}$, 5
$A \cap B$, 5
$\bigcap_{i=m}^{n} A_i$, 5
$\bigcap_{i \in I} A_i$, 5
$\bigcap F$, 5
$A \sim B$, 5
$A \times B$, 6
S^n, 11
$\prod_{i=m}^{n} S_i$, 11
S^I, 11
$\prod_{i \in I} S_i$, 11
$\mathscr{R}_n$, 12
$\boldsymbol{\ell}_p$, 12
$\|x\|_p$, 12
$\langle x, y \rangle$, 12
$\mathbf{B}(S)$, 13
$\mathbf{C}(S)$, 13
$\mathbf{C}^n(S)$, 13
$\mathbf{C}^\infty(S)$, 13
$\mathbf{S}_\rho(r, x)$, 17
$\text{diam}_\rho\, A$, 17
$\text{dist}_\rho\, (A, B)$, 17
interior A, 21, 23
nbhd x, 21, 23
boundary A, 21, 23
closure A, 21, 23
$x_n \xrightarrow{n} \ell$, 27
component x, 40
$y \doteq \lim_{t \to x} f(t)$, 44
S^*, 51
$\mathscr{L}(\mathscr{G})$, 51
$\overline{\mathscr{R}}$, $\overline{\mathscr{R}}_+$, 57
$\sum_{n \in A} x_n$, 58
H_σ, H_δ, 59
ring H, 59
field H, 59
Borel ring H, 59
Borel field H, 59
$\text{var}^+\, \mu(A)$, 63
$\text{var}^-\, \mu(A)$, 63
$\text{var}\, \mu(A)$, 63
$\mathscr{M}_\mu$, 66
$\boldsymbol{\tau}_n$, 79
$\boldsymbol{\lambda}_n$, 79
f^+, f^-, 85
f_A, 85
region under f, 85
$\int^* f\, d\mu$, $\int_A^* f\, d\mu$, 85
$\int_\mu^* f(x)\, dx$, $\int_{\mu;A}^* f(x)\, dx$, 85
$\mathbf{SF}(\mathfrak{A})$, $\mathbf{SF}_\mu$, 86
$\mathscr{P}(\mathfrak{A})$, $\mathscr{P}_\mu$, 86
$\mathbf{MF}(\mathfrak{A})$, $\mathbf{MF}_\mu$, 86
$\int f\, d\mu$, 87, 119
μ-a.a. $x \in A$, 89
$\mathscr{L}_p^*(\mu)$, $\mathscr{L}_p(\mu)$, 101
$g \doteq \lim_n f_n \quad \mu\text{-}ae$, 101
$g \doteq \lim_n f_n$ in μ, 101
$\mathbf{I}(x)$, 114
$\mathfrak{A}_0$, 118
$\mathbf{LS}$, $\mathbf{LS}_+$, 118
$\mathbf{V}(f; a, b)$, 121
$\mathbf{D}f(x)$, 121
$\int_a^b f(x)\, dx$, 121
$\mathbf{BV}$, 121
$\mathbf{AC}$, 121
$\mathbf{C}_0(A)$, $\mathbf{C}_0^+(A)$, 126
$\mathbf{C}_0^*$, $\mathbf{C}_0^{*+}$, 126
$\|\ell\|_A$, 126

INDEX

Absolutely continuous function, 117, 121
  measure, 110
Absolutely measurable set, 119
Accumulation point, 27
Additive, 59
Almost all, 89
Ascoli-Arzela theorem, 50

Baire category, 38
Banach space, 53
Base for a topology, 29
Bilinear form, 14
Borel ring, field, 59
Boundary, 21, 23
Bounded set, 17

Cantor theorem, 8
  function, 117
    set, 35
Cantor-Bendixon theorem, 31
Cantor-Schröder-Bernstein theorem, 8
Carathéodory measure, 66
Cartesian product, 6, 11
Category, first and second, 38
Cauchy sequence, 32
Cauchy-Schwarz inequality, 14
Cavalieri's principle, 98
Closed set, 21, 23
Closure, 21, 23
Compact, 35
Complete, 32
Completion, 33
Component, 40
Conditional probability, 111
Connected, 40
Constant function, 5
Continuous function, 43
Convergence of a sequence, 27
  almost everywhere, 101
    in measure, 101
    mean, square mean, 18, 101
    pointwise, 24, 47, 51
    uniform, 18, 24, 47
Countable base, 29
  set, 7
Covering, 5
  open, 29

Daniell integral, 104
Darboux sum, 88
Decomposition theorems:
  Hahn, 107
  Jordan, 63
  Lebesgue, 110
Denjoy integral, 105
Dense set, 29
Density of a set at a point, 117
Derivative, 106
  ordinary, 114, 117, 121
  Radón-Nikodym, 109, 110
Diameter, 17
Distance, 17
Domain, 4
Dominated convergence theorem, 95
Dual of a vector space, 52
  of ℓ_p, 53
  of $\mathscr{L}_p$, 111, 112

Egoroff theorem, 103
Element of a set, 3
Empty set, 3
Equicontinuous family of functions, 48, 49
Equivalent metric, norm, 23
Euclidean space $\mathscr{R}^n$, 11
  $\mathscr{R}_n$, 12
Extended real line $\overline{\mathscr{R}}$, 57

Fatou's lemma, 95
Field, 59

Finite set, 7
Fubini theorem, 98
Functive, 5
Function spaces, 10, 13
Functional, 51

Hahn decomposition theorem, 107
Hausdorff topology, 25
    one-dimensional measure, 125
Heine-Borel theorem, 35
Hölder inequality, 15
Homeomorphism, 46

Iff, 3
Infinite set, 7
Inner measure, 72
    product, 12, 14
Integrable, 86
Integral: outer or upper, 85
    of a measurable function, 87
    w.r.t. a signed measure, 119
Interior, 21, 23
Intersection, 5
Interval, 4, 58
Isolated point, 27

Jordan decomposition theorem, 63

Lebsegue decomposition theorem, 110
    dominated convergence theorem, 95
    measure, 78, 79
    measurable set, 78, 80
    non-measurable set, 79
Lebesgue-Stieltjes measure, 74
Length, 125
Limit point of a sequence, 27
    of a function, 44
    pointwise, 47
    uniform, 47
Lindelöf, 29
Linear functional, 51, 126
    measure, 125
ℓ_p spaces, 12
$\mathscr{L}_p$ spaces, 101
Lusin theorem, 102

Measurable function, 86
    set, 66
Measure, 59
    Carathéodory, 66
    counting, 71
    image of, 71
    inner, 72
    Lebesgue, 78, 79
    Lebesgue-Stieltjes, 74
    outer, 66, 72
    point mass, 71
    Radón, 78
    trivial, 70
Metric, 17
    induced by a norm, 18
Minkowski's inequality, 15
Monotone convergence theorem, 94

Natural numbers, ω, 4
Neighborhood in metric space, 21
    in topological space, 23
    of $\pm\infty$, 58
Nondecreasing function, 74
Nonmeasurable set, 79
Norm, 14
    in ℓ_p, 12
    in $\mathscr{L}_p$, 101
    sup norm, 13
Normal topology, 25
Nowhere dense set, 38
n-tuple, 11

One-to-one, 5
Onto, 5
Open set, 21, 23
Ordered pair, 4
Outer integral, 85
    measure, 66, 72

Partition, 86
Perfect set, 27
Pointwise convergence, 24, 47, 51
Power, 7
Product measure, 85, 100
    space, 6, 11
    topology, 51

Pseudo-inner product, 14
 metric, 17
 norm, 14, 101

Radón outer measure, 78
Radón-Nikodym derivative, 106
 theorem, 110
Range, 4
Rationals, $\mathscr{R}$a, 4
Real line $\mathscr{R}$, 4
 extended $\overline{\mathscr{R}}$, 57
Rectangle, 79
Regular topology, 25
Relation, 4
Relative topology, 23
Restriction of a measure, 11
 of a topology, 23
Riemann integral, 94, 104
 sum, 93
Riesz representation theorem, 129
Ring, 59

Second axiom of countability, 29
Separable, 29
Sequence, 12
 Cauchy, 32
Set, 3
Signed measure, 119
Singular function, 121
 measure, 110
Sphere, 17
Step function, 86
Subsequence, 12
Summable function, 87
Sup norm, 13
σ-additive, 59
σ-field, 59
σ-finite, 89
σ-ring, 59

Tietze's theorem, 45
Topology, 22, 23
 discrete, 24
 of pointwise convergence, 24, 29, 51
 of uniform convergence, 24
 on $\overline{\mathscr{R}}$, 58
 trivial, 24
Totally bounded set, 17

Uncountable, 7
Uniform continuity, 45
 convergence, 24, 47
 equicontinuity, 49
Union, 5
Universally measurable set, 119
Unordered sum, 58

Variation of a real function, 64, 121
 of a set function, 63
Vector space, 13
Vitali covering theorem, 112
 property, 113
Vitali-Lusin theorem, 102

Weierstrass theorem, 30